2003 | Intermediate I

[BLANK PAGE]

FOR OFFICIAL USE

Total mark

X100/101

NATIONAL QUALIFICATIONS 2003

WEDNESDAY, 21 MAY
1.30 PM – 2.05 PM

MATHEMATICS
INTERMEDIATE 1
Units 1, 2 and 3
Paper 1
(Non-calculator)

Fill in these boxes and read what is printed below.

Full name of centre

Town

Forename(s)

Surname

Date of birth
Day Month Year

Scottish candidate number

Number of seat

1 **You may NOT use a calculator.**

2 Write your working and answers in the spaces provided. Additional space is provided at the end of this question-answer book for use if required. If you use this space, write clearly the number of the question involved.

3 Full credit will be given only where the solution contains appropriate working.

4 Before leaving the examination room you must give this book to the invigilator. If you do not you may lose all the marks for this paper.

LIB X100/101 6/3/11770

FORMULAE LIST

Circumference of a circle: $C = \pi d$

Area of a circle: $A = \pi r^2$

Theorem of Pythagoras:

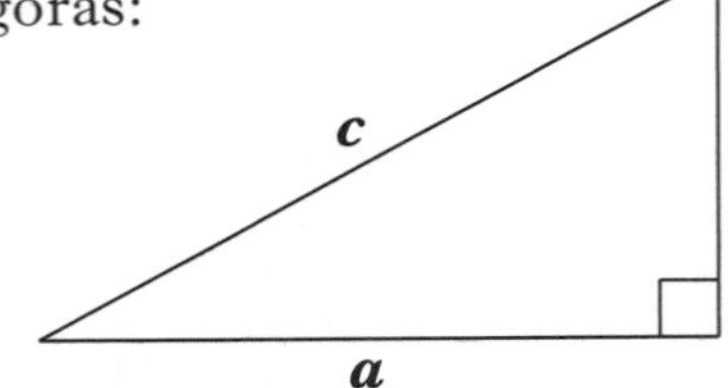

$a^2 + b^2 = c^2$

Trigonometric ratios in a right angled triangle:

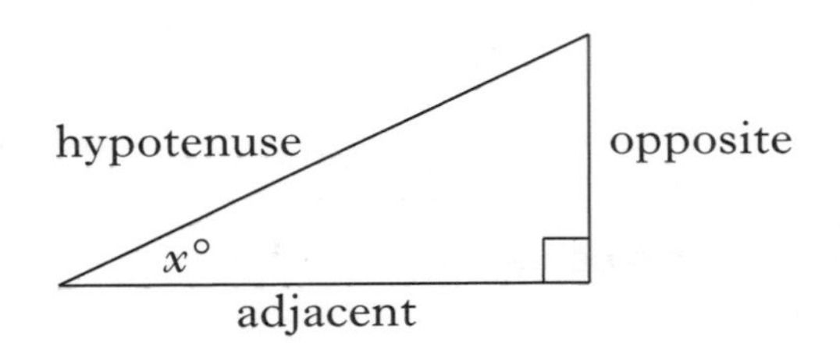

$$\tan x^\circ = \frac{\textbf{opposite}}{\textbf{adjacent}}$$

$$\sin x^\circ = \frac{\textbf{opposite}}{\textbf{hypotenuse}}$$

$$\cos x^\circ = \frac{\textbf{adjacent}}{\textbf{hypotenuse}}$$

DO NOT WRITE IN THIS MARGIN

Marks

ALL questions should be attempted.

1. (*a*) Find $6 \cdot 23 - 3 \cdot 7$. **1**

(*b*) Find 5% of £140. **1**

(*c*) Find $-40 + 15$. **1**

2. A rule used to calculate the cost in pounds of electricity is:

Cost = 19 + (number of units used × 0·07)

Find the cost of 600 units of electricity. **2**

[Turn over

DO NOT WRITE IN THIS MARGIN

Marks

3. (*a*) An inter-city coach left Aberdeen at 10.40 am and reached Inverness at 1.25 pm.

How long did the journey take? **1**

(*b*) The average speed of the coach during the journey was 40 miles per hour.

Find the distance between Aberdeen and Inverness. **3**

4. Solve algebraically the equation

$$8c + 3 = 31 + c.$$

3

DO NOT WRITE IN THIS MARGIN

Marks

5. Andy wants to make 150 copies of a music booklet.
8 sheets of paper are required for each booklet.

(*a*) Find the total number of sheets required. **1**

Paper is sold in packets which contain 500 sheets.

(*b*) How many packets of paper will Andy need to buy? **2**

6. Solve algebraically the inequality

$$9m - 2 > 70.$$

2

[Turn over

DO NOT WRITE IN THIS MARGIN

Marks

7. (*a*) Complete the table below for $y = 1 \cdot 5x - 1$.

x	−2	0	6
y			

2

(*b*) Draw the line $y = 1 \cdot 5x - 1$ on the grid.

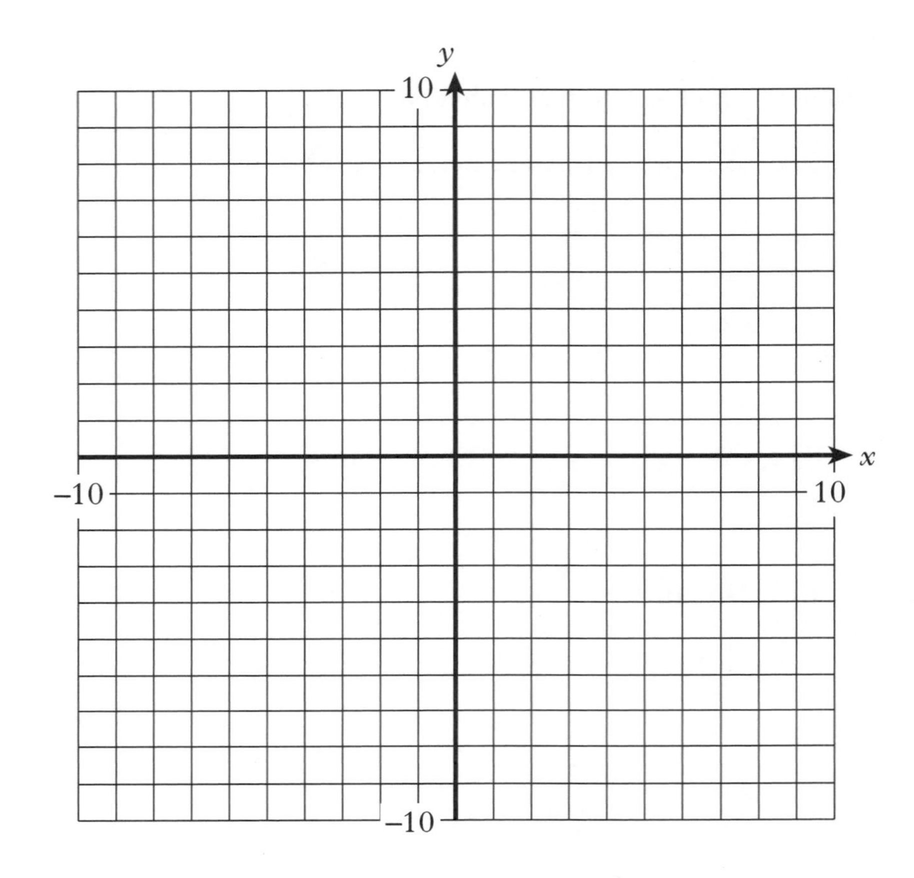

2

DO NOT WRITE IN THIS MARGIN

Marks

8. In a local election the number of votes for each of the four candidates is shown in the table below.

Candidate	*Votes*
Smith	380
Patel	240
Green	100
Jones	170

On the grid below, draw a bar graph to show this information.

4

9. Five staff work in an office.

Three of them are female.

What percentage of the staff is female?

3

DO NOT WRITE IN THIS MARGIN

Marks

10. This is a multiplication square.

8	×	5	=	40
×		×		×
10	×	–2	=	–20
=		=		=
80	×	–10	=	–800

(*a*) Complete this multiplication square.

3	×	–7	=	
×		×		×
–1	×	5	=	
=		=		=
	×		=	

2

DO NOT WRITE IN THIS MARGIN

Marks

10. (continued)

(*b*) Complete this multiplication square.

–5	×		=	
×		×		×
	×		=	–12
=		=		=
	×	–8	=	–120

3

[*END OF QUESTION PAPER*]

DO NOT WRITE IN THIS MARGIN

ADDITIONAL SPACE FOR ANSWERS

FOR OFFICIAL USE

Total mark

X100/103

NATIONAL QUALIFICATIONS 2003

WEDNESDAY, 21 MAY
2.25 PM – 3.20 PM

MATHEMATICS
INTERMEDIATE 1
Units 1, 2 and 3
Paper 2

Fill in these boxes and read what is printed below.

Full name of centre

Town

Forename(s)

Surname

Date of birth
Day Month Year

Scottish candidate number

Number of seat

1 **You may use a calculator.**

2 Write your working and answers in the spaces provided. Additional space is provided at the end of this question-answer book for use if required. If you use this space, write clearly the number of the question involved.

3 Full credit will be given only where the solution contains appropriate working.

4 Before leaving the examination room you must give this book to the invigilator. If you do not you may lose all the marks for this paper.

FORMULAE LIST

Circumference of a circle: $C = \pi d$

Area of a circle: $A = \pi r^2$

Theorem of Pythagoras:

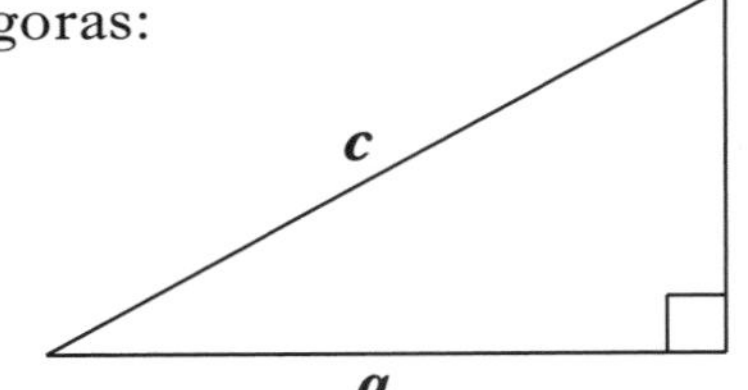

$$a^2 + b^2 = c^2$$

Trigonometric ratios in a right angled triangle:

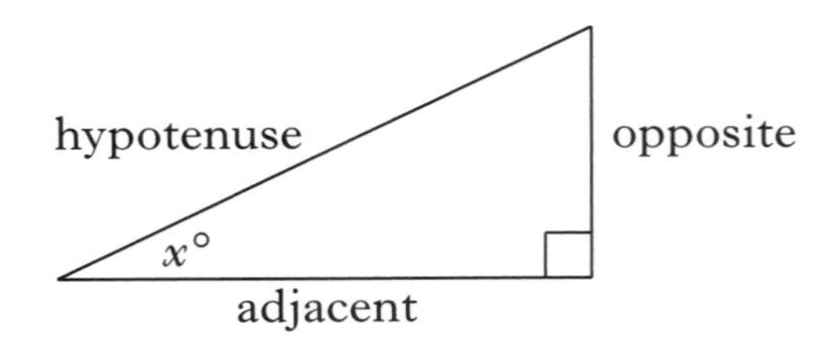

$$\tan x° = \frac{\text{opposite}}{\text{adjacent}}$$

$$\sin x° = \frac{\text{opposite}}{\text{hypotenuse}}$$

$$\cos x° = \frac{\text{adjacent}}{\text{hypotenuse}}$$

DO NOT WRITE IN THIS MARGIN

Marks

ALL questions should be attempted.

1. A day in December is chosen at random for a youth club outing.
Find the probability that a **Saturday** is chosen.

DECEMBER

Mon	Tue	Wed	Thu	Fri	Sat	Sun
1	2	3	4	5	6	7
8	9	10	11	12	13	14
15	16	17	18	19	20	21
22	23	24	25	26	27	28
29	30	31				

1

2. A common cold virus is 5×10^{-4} millimetres long.
Write this number in full.

2

[Turn over

DO NOT WRITE IN THIS MARGIN

Marks

3. (*a*) Multiply out the brackets and simplify

$$5(a + 2b) - 3b.$$

2

(*b*) Factorise $6n + 30$.

2

Marks

4. The income of each employee in a company is shown in this frequency table.

Income £	*Frequency*	*Income × Frequency*
10 000	2	
12 000	3	
14 000	5	
16 000	8	
18 000	7	
	Total = 25	Total =

(*a*) Write down the modal income. **1**

(*b*) Complete the table above and find the mean income. **3**

[Turn over

DO NOT WRITE IN THIS MARGIN

Marks

5. A room in the Hotel Royale in Paris costs 130 euros per night.
The exchange rate is 1·58 euros to the pound.

(*a*) Find the cost of the hotel room per night in pounds and pence. **3**

Mr and Mrs McQueen are going to Paris.
Their return flights cost £59 each.

(*b*) Find the total cost of their flights and a 3 night stay at the Hotel Royale in pounds and pence. **2**

DO NOT WRITE IN THIS MARGIN

Marks

6. The population of Scotland in 2001 was 5 062 000.

The pie chart shows the age distribution of the population in 2001.

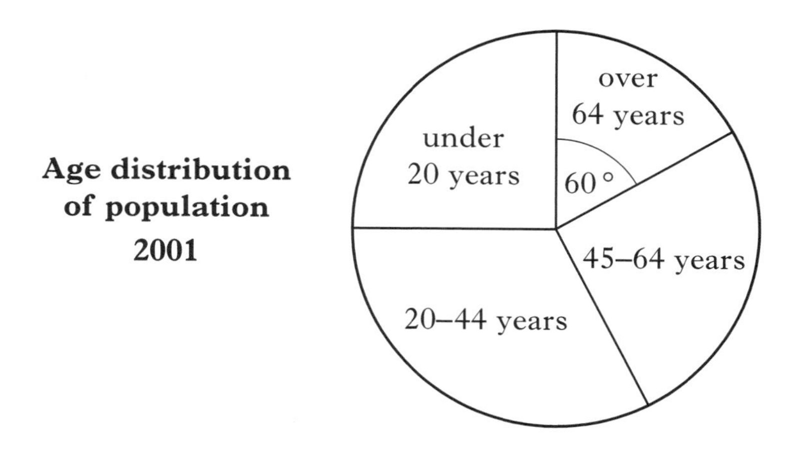

(*a*) How many people were aged over 64 years?

Give your answer to the nearest thousand. **3**

(*b*) The pie chart below shows the age distribution of the population of Scotland in 1901.

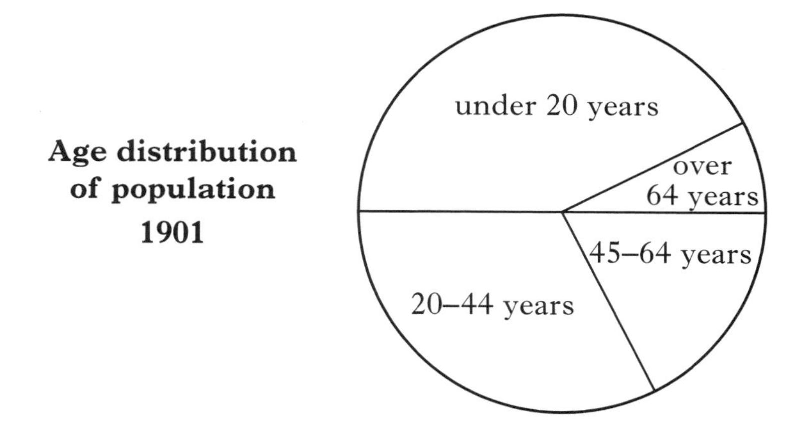

Describe the differences in the age distributions of the population of Scotland in 1901 and 2001. **2**

DO NOT WRITE IN THIS MARGIN

Marks

7. The diagram below shows two bars of soap.
Each bar is in the shape of a cuboid.

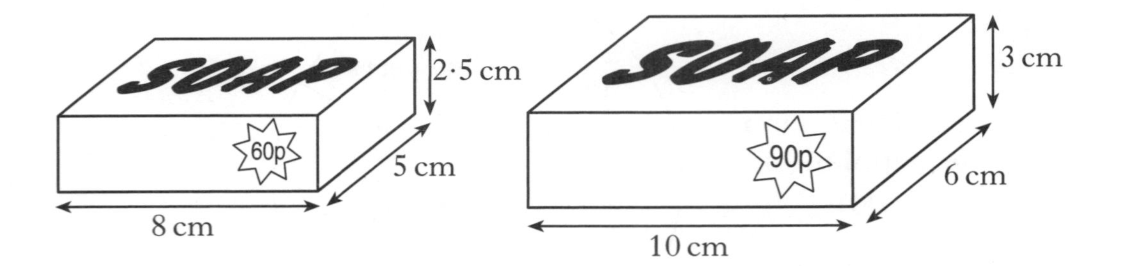

(*a*) Find the volume of the smaller bar. **1**

(*b*) The smaller bar costs 60 pence.
Find the cost per cubic centimetre of the smaller bar. **1**

(*c*) The larger bar costs 90 pence.
Which bar of soap gives better value for money?
Explain clearly the reason for your answer. **3**

Marks

8. Use the formula below to find the value of R when $P = 180$, $M = 7{\cdot}5$ and $N = 5$.

$$R = \frac{P}{MN}$$

3

9. The diagram shows the front view of a garage.

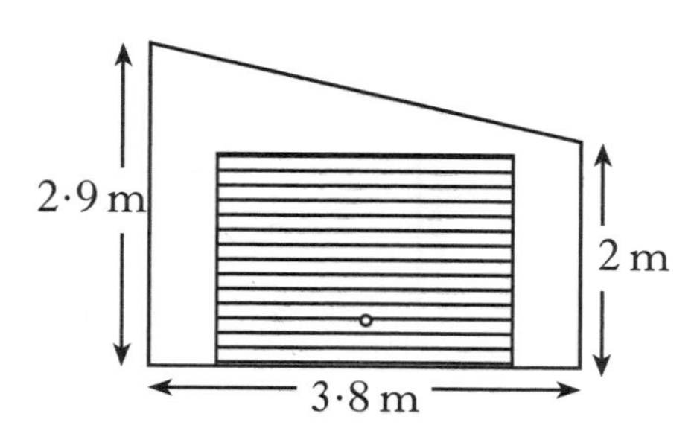

Calculate the length of the sloping edge of the roof.
Do not use a scale drawing.

3

[Turn over

DO NOT WRITE IN THIS MARGIN

Marks

10. Gail wants to insure her computer for £2400.

The insurance company charges an annual premium of £1·25 for each £100 insured.

(*a*) Calculate the annual premium. **2**

(*b*) Gail can pay her premium monthly.

If she does this she is charged an extra 4%.

Calculate the monthly premium. **3**

DO NOT WRITE IN THIS MARGIN

Marks

11. A television mast is supported by wires.

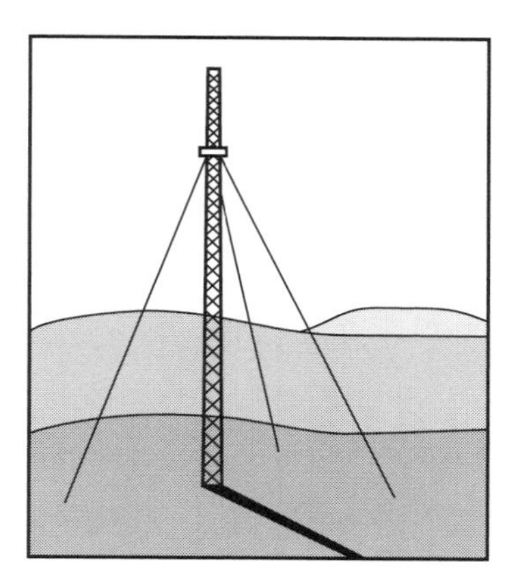

The diagram below shows one of the wires which is 80 metres long. The wire is attached to the mast 20 metres from the top and makes an angle of 59° with the ground.

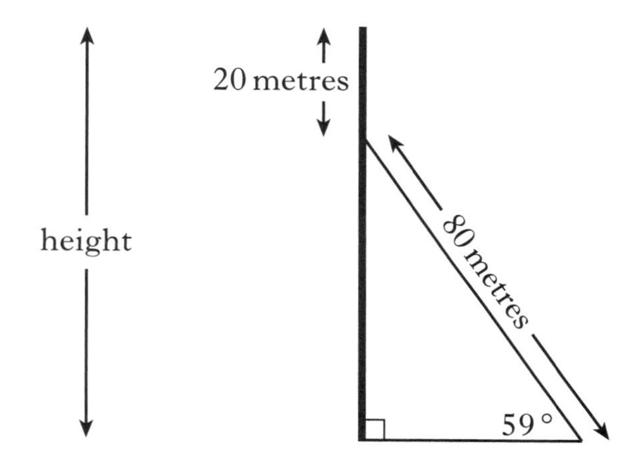

Calculate the height of the mast.

Give your answer to the nearest metre.

Do not use a scale drawing.

5

[Turn over for Question 12 on *Page twelve*

DO NOT WRITE IN THIS MARGIN

Marks

12. The diagram below shows a window.

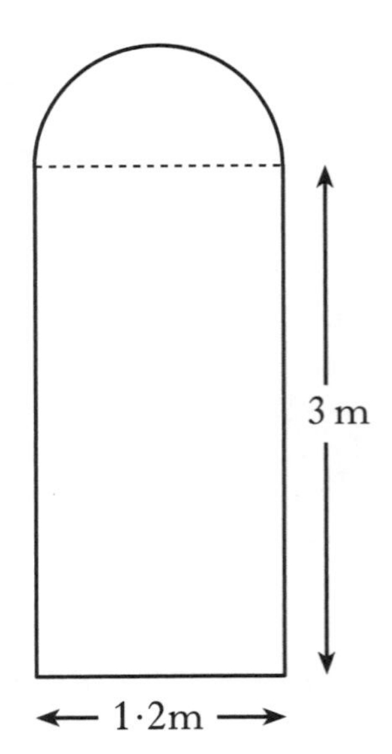

The window consists of a rectangle and a semi-circle.

Calculate the area of the window.

Give your answer in square metres correct to 2 decimal places.

5

[*END OF QUESTION PAPER*]

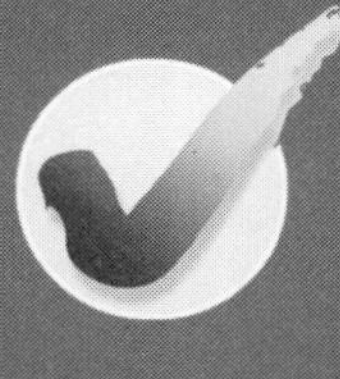

2004 | Intermediate 1

[BLANK PAGE]

FOR OFFICIAL USE

Total mark

X100/101

NATIONAL QUALIFICATIONS 2004

FRIDAY, 21 MAY
1.00 PM – 1.35 PM

MATHEMATICS
INTERMEDIATE 1
Units 1, 2 and 3
Paper 1
(Non-calculator)

Fill in these boxes and read what is printed below.

Full name of centre

Town

Forename(s)

Surname

Date of birth
Day Month Year

Scottish candidate number

Number of seat

1 **You may NOT use a calculator.**

2 Write your working and answers in the spaces provided. Additional space is provided at the end of this question-answer book for use if required. If you use this space, write clearly the number of the question involved.

3 Full credit will be given only where the solution contains appropriate working.

4 Before leaving the examination room you must give this book to the invigilator. If you do not you may lose all the marks for this paper.

LIB X100/101 6/10520

FORMULAE LIST

Circumference of a circle: $C = \pi d$

Area of a circle: $A = \pi r^2$

Theorem of Pythagoras:

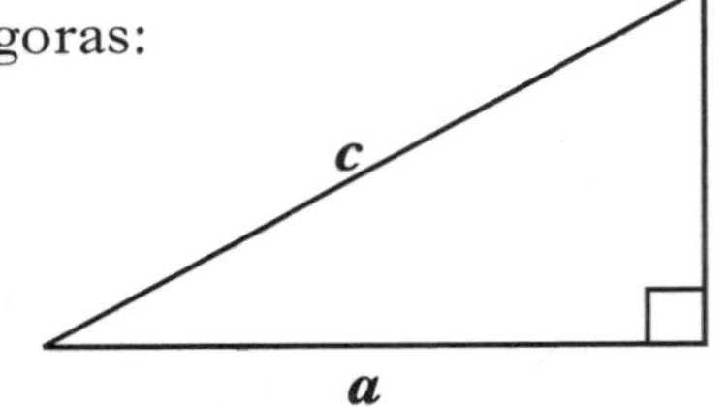

$$a^2 + b^2 = c^2$$

Trigonometric ratios in a right angled triangle:

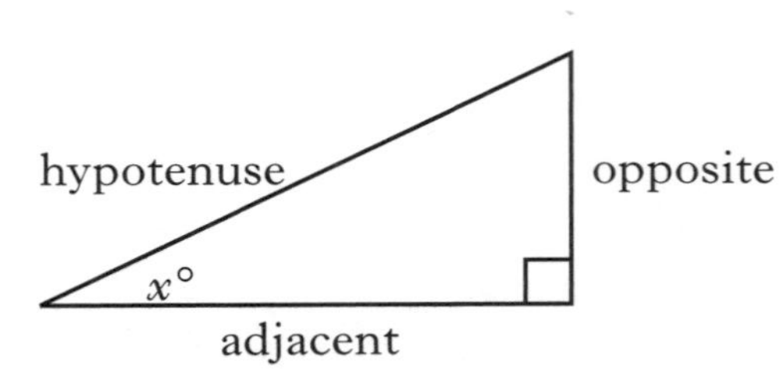

$$\tan x^\circ = \frac{\text{opposite}}{\text{adjacent}}$$

$$\sin x^\circ = \frac{\text{opposite}}{\text{hypotenuse}}$$

$$\cos x^\circ = \frac{\text{adjacent}}{\text{hypotenuse}}$$

DO NOT WRITE IN THIS MARGIN

Marks

ALL questions should be attempted.

1. Work out the answers to the following.

(*a*) 30% of £230 **1**

(*b*) $\frac{4}{7}$ of 105 **1**

(*c*) $380 - 20 \times 9$ **1**

2. A cooker can be bought by paying a deposit of £59 followed by 12 instalments of £45.

Calculate the total price of the cooker. **2**

[Turn over

DO NOT WRITE IN THIS MARGIN

Marks

3. Calculate the volume of this cuboid.

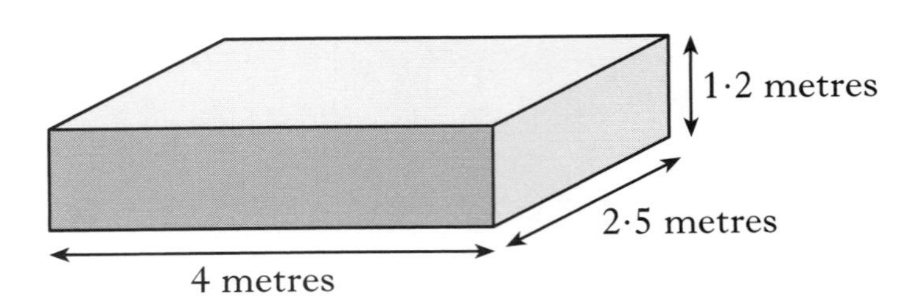

2

4. The temperatures, in degrees Celsius, at noon for the first ten days in January at Invergow were:

$-3 \quad 0 \quad -2 \quad 2 \quad -1 \quad -4 \quad -5 \quad -3 \quad 1 \quad 3.$

Calculate

(*a*) the median temperature; **2**

(*b*) the range. **2**

DO NOT WRITE IN THIS MARGIN

Marks

4. (continued)

(*c*) The corresponding values of the median and the range for Abergrange are 2 °C and 5 °C respectively.

Make **two** comments comparing the temperatures in Invergow and Abergrange.

2

5. Solve algebraically the equation

$$11 + 5x = 2x + 29.$$

3

[Turn over

DO NOT WRITE IN THIS MARGIN

Marks

6. A shop sells artificial flowers.
The prices of individual flowers are shown below.

Variety	**Price**
Carnation	£2
Daffodil	£3·50
Lily	£4
Iris	£3
Rose	£4·50

Zara wants to
- buy 3 flowers
- choose 3 different varieties
- spend a **minimum** of £10.

One combination of flowers that Zara can buy is shown in the table below.

Carnation	Daffodil	Lily	Iris	Rose	Total Price
		✓	✓	✓	£11·50

Complete the table to show **all** the possible combinations that Zara can buy. **3**

DO NOT WRITE IN THIS MARGIN

Marks

7. An Internet provider has a customer helpline.
The length of each telephone call to the helpline was recorded one day.
The results are shown in the frequency table below.

Length of call (to nearest minute)	Frequency	Length of call × Frequency
1	15	15
2	40	80
3	26	78
4	29	116
5	49	
6	41	
	Total = 200	Total =

(*a*) Complete the table above and find the mean length of call. **3**

(*b*) Write down the modal length of call. **1**

[Turn over

DO NOT WRITE IN THIS MARGIN

Marks

8. (*a*) Complete the table below for $y = 3 - x$.

x	-2	2	7
y			

2

(*b*) Draw the line $y = 3 - x$ on the grid.

y
10
−10
10
x
−10

2

DO NOT WRITE IN THIS MARGIN

Marks

9. One billion is 1000 million.

A country borrows 2×10^{10} dollars.

How many billions of dollars is this?

3

10. Evaluate $\frac{2xy}{z}$ when $x = -5$, $y = 6$ and $z = -4$.

3

[*END OF QUESTION PAPER*]

DO NOT WRITE IN THIS MARGIN

ADDITIONAL SPACE FOR ANSWERS

FOR OFFICIAL USE

Total mark

X100/103

NATIONAL QUALIFICATIONS 2004

FRIDAY, 21 MAY
1.55 PM – 2.50 PM

MATHEMATICS
INTERMEDIATE 1
Units 1, 2 and 3
Paper 2

Fill in these boxes and read what is printed below.

Full name of centre

Town

Forename(s)

Surname

Date of birth
Day Month Year

Scottish candidate number

Number of seat

1 **You may use a calculator.**

2 Write your working and answers in the spaces provided. Additional space is provided at the end of this question-answer book for use if required. If you use this space, write clearly the number of the question involved.

3 Full credit will be given only where the solution contains appropriate working.

4 Before leaving the examination room you must give this book to the invigilator. If you do not you may lose all the marks for this paper.

FORMULAE LIST

Circumference of a circle: $C = \pi d$

Area of a circle: $A = \pi r^2$

Theorem of Pythagoras:

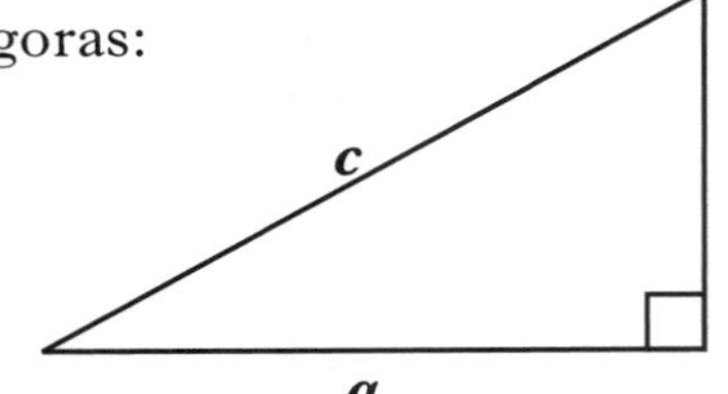

$a^2 + b^2 = c^2$

Trigonometric ratios in a right angled triangle:

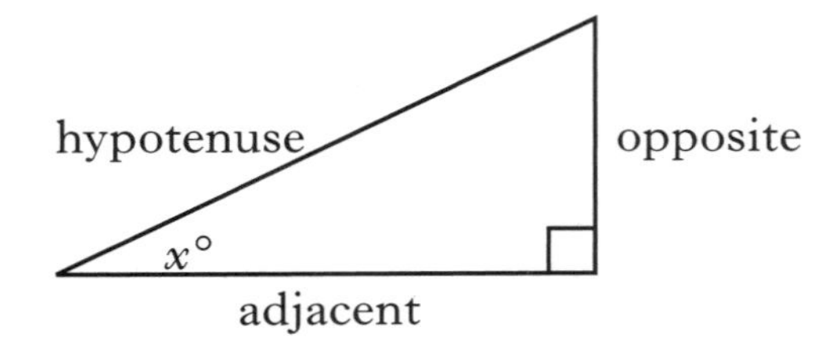

$$\tan x° = \frac{\textbf{opposite}}{\textbf{adjacent}}$$

$$\sin x° = \frac{\textbf{opposite}}{\textbf{hypotenuse}}$$

$$\cos x° = \frac{\textbf{adjacent}}{\textbf{hypotenuse}}$$

DO NOT WRITE IN THIS MARGIN

Marks

ALL questions should be attempted.

1. 2000 tickets are sold for a raffle in which the star prize is a television.
   Kirsty buys 10 tickets for the raffle.
   What is the probability that she wins the star prize?

   1

2. (*a*) On the grid below, plot the points A(–3, 4), B(2, 4) and C(6, –5).

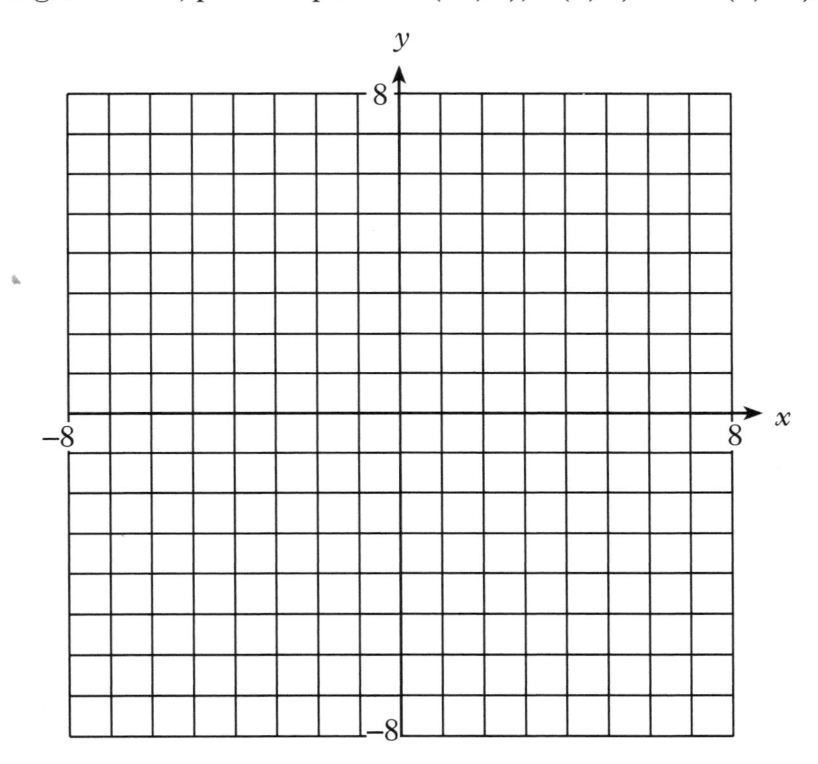

   2

   (*b*) Plot the point D so that shape ABCD is a kite.
   Write down the coordinates of point D.

   2

[Turn over

DO NOT WRITE IN THIS MARGIN

Marks

3. An overnight train left London at 2040 and reached Inverness at 0810 the next day.

The distance travelled by the train was 552 miles.

Calculate the average speed of the train.

3

4. Solve algebraically the inequality

$$8n - 3 < 37.$$

2

DO NOT WRITE IN THIS MARGIN

Marks

5. The scattergraph shows the age and mileage of cars in a garage.

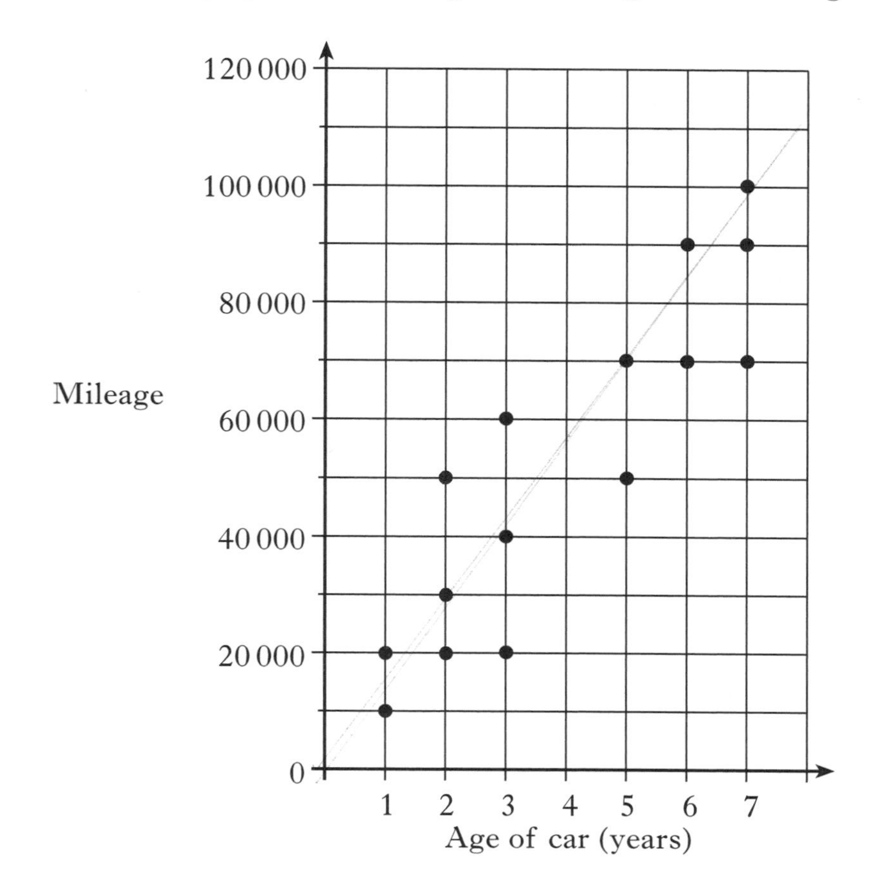

(*a*) Draw a line of best fit through the points on the graph. **1**

(*b*) Use your line of best fit to estimate the mileage of a 4 year old car. **1**

6. (*a*) Multiply out the brackets and simplify

$$2(4 - t) + 5t.$$

2

(*b*) Factorise $10y - 35$. **2**

DO NOT WRITE IN THIS MARGIN

Marks

7. Ryan wants to take out a life insurance policy.
The insurance company charges a monthly premium of £2·50 for each £1000 of cover.
Ryan can afford to pay £90 per month.
How much cover can he get?

2

8. (*a*) In a jewellery shop the price of a gold chain is proportional to its length.
A 16 inch gold chain is priced at £40.
Calculate the price of a 24 inch gold chain.

2

(*b*) The gold chains are displayed diagonally on a **square** board of side 20 inches.
The longest chain stretches from corner to corner.
Calculate the length of the longest chain.
Do not use a scale drawing.

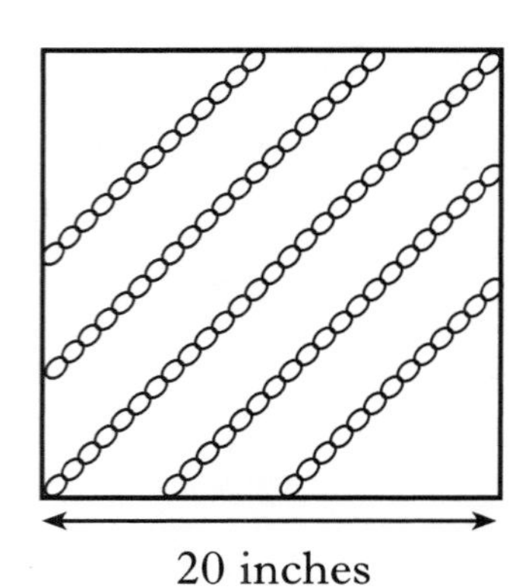

3

DO NOT WRITE IN THIS MARGIN

Marks

9. Andy buys a bottle of aftershave in Spain for 38·50 euros.
The same bottle of aftershave costs £25·99 in Scotland.
The exchange rate is £1 = 1·52 euros.
Does he save money by buying the aftershave in Spain?
Explain your answer.

3

10. The front of the tent shown below is an isosceles triangle.

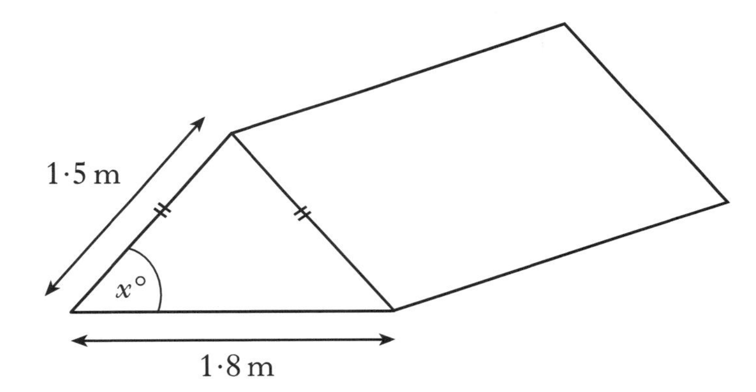

The size of the angle between the side and the bottom of the tent is $x°$.
Calculate x.

4

DO NOT WRITE IN THIS MARGIN

Marks

11. The graph below shows how the rate of interest for a savings account with the Clydeside Bank changed during 2002.

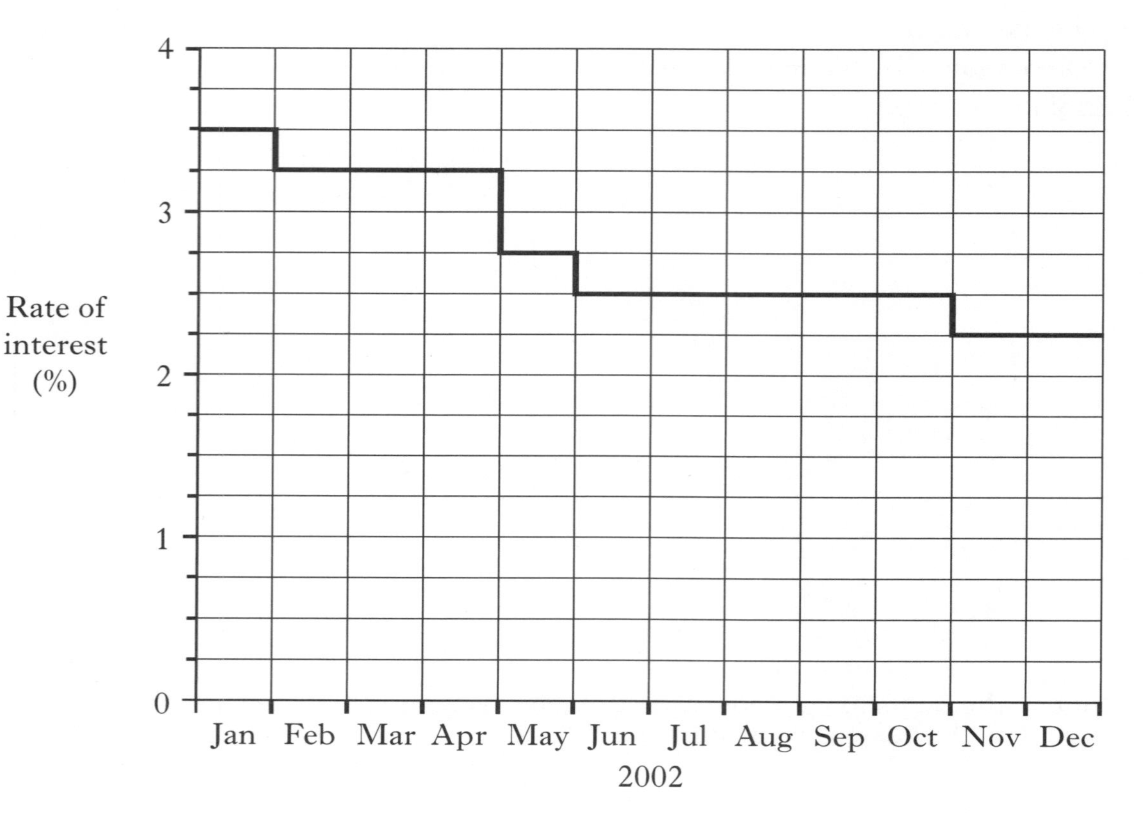

(*a*) What was the interest rate in March? **1**

(*b*) Describe the trend of the interest rate during the year. **1**

(*c*) In June £1400 was invested in this account.
How much interest was due after 3 months? **4**

DO NOT WRITE IN THIS MARGIN

Marks

12. The minimum velocity v metres per second, allowed at the top of a loop in a roller coaster, is given by the formula

$$v = \sqrt{gr}$$

where r metres is the radius of the loop.

Calculate the value of v when $g = 9{\cdot}81$ and $r = 9$.

3

13. 40 people were asked whether they preferred tea or coffee.
18 of them said they preferred coffee.
What percentage said they preferred coffee?

3

[Turn over

DO NOT WRITE IN THIS MARGIN

Marks

14. The diagram below shows a rectangular door with a window.

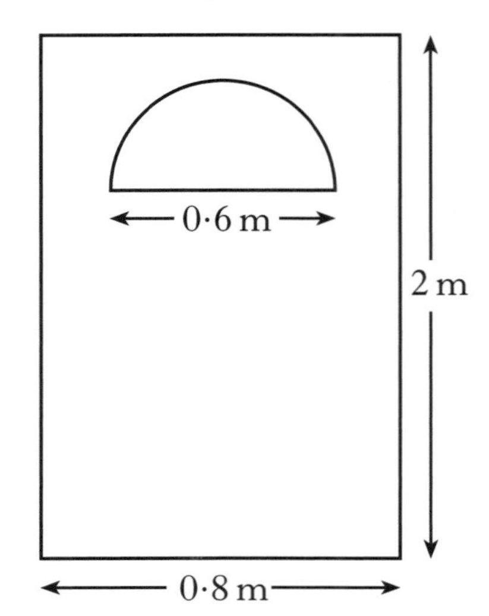

The window is in the shape of a semi-circle and is made of glass.

The rest of the door is made of wood.

Calculate the area of the wooden part of the door.

Give your answer in square metres correct to two decimal places.

5

[*END OF QUESTION PAPER*]

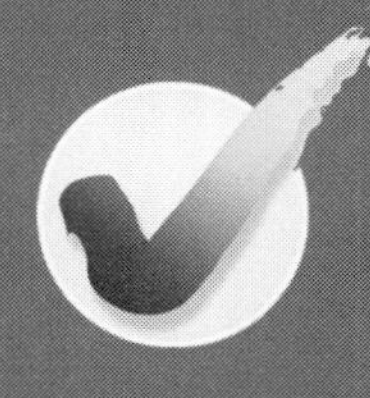

[BLANK PAGE]

FOR OFFICIAL USE

Total mark

X100/101

NATIONAL QUALIFICATIONS 2005

FRIDAY, 20 MAY
1.00 PM – 1.35 PM

MATHEMATICS
INTERMEDIATE 1
Units 1, 2 and 3
Paper 1
(Non-calculator)

Fill in these boxes and read what is printed below.

Full name of centre

Town

Forename(s)

Surname

Date of birth
Day Month Year

Scottish candidate number

Number of seat

1 **You may NOT use a calculator.**

2 Write your working and answers in the spaces provided. Additional space is provided at the end of this question-answer book for use if required. If you use this space, write clearly the number of the question involved.

3 Full credit will be given only where the solution contains appropriate working.

4 Before leaving the examination room you must give this book to the invigilator. If you do not you may lose all the marks for this paper.

LIB X100/101 6/11870

FORMULAE LIST

Circumference of a circle: $C = \pi d$

Area of a circle: $A = \pi r^2$

Theorem of Pythagoras:

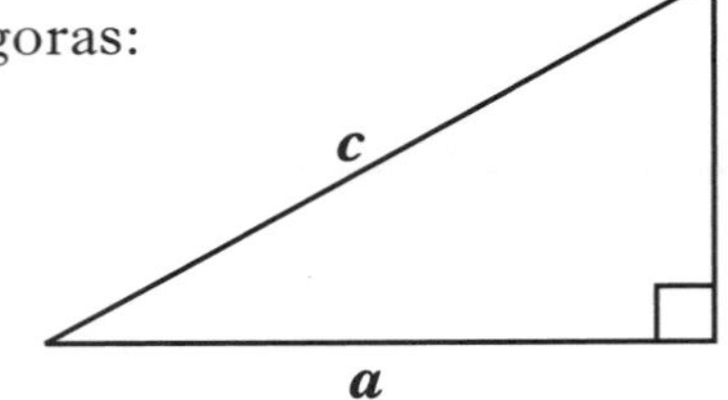

$a^2 + b^2 = c^2$

Trigonometric ratios in a right angled triangle:

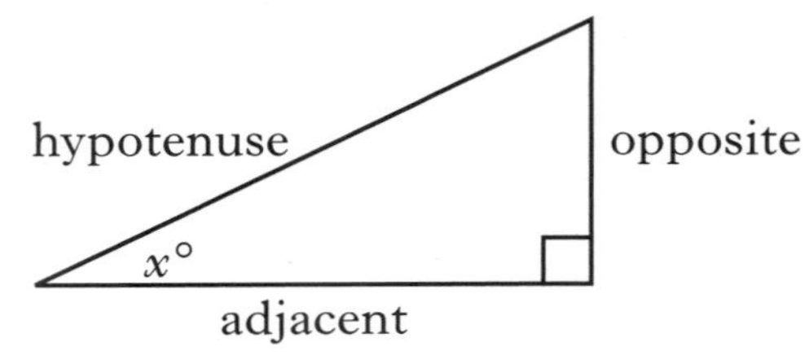

$\tan x^\circ = \dfrac{\text{opposite}}{\text{adjacent}}$

$\sin x^\circ = \dfrac{\text{opposite}}{\text{hypotenuse}}$

$\cos x^\circ = \dfrac{\text{adjacent}}{\text{hypotenuse}}$

DO NOT WRITE IN THIS MARGIN

Marks

ALL questions should be attempted.

1. (*a*) Find 6·17 – 2·3. **1**

(*b*) Find 75% of £1200. **1**

2. Joyce is going on holiday. She must be at the airport by 1.20 pm. It takes her 4 hours 30 minutes to travel from home to the airport. What is the latest time that she should leave home for the airport? **1**

[Turn over

DO NOT WRITE IN THIS MARGIN

Marks

3. A regular polygon is a shape with three or more equal sides.

Examples of regular polygons

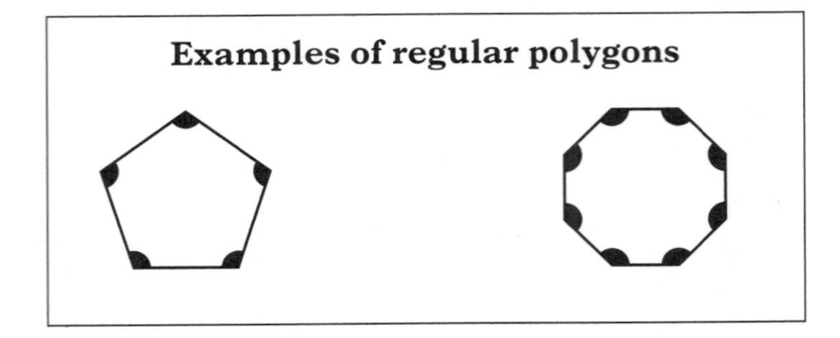

A rule used to calculate the size, in degrees, of each angle in a regular polygon is:

Size of each angle = 180 – (360 ÷ number of sides)

Calculate the size of each angle in the regular polygon below.

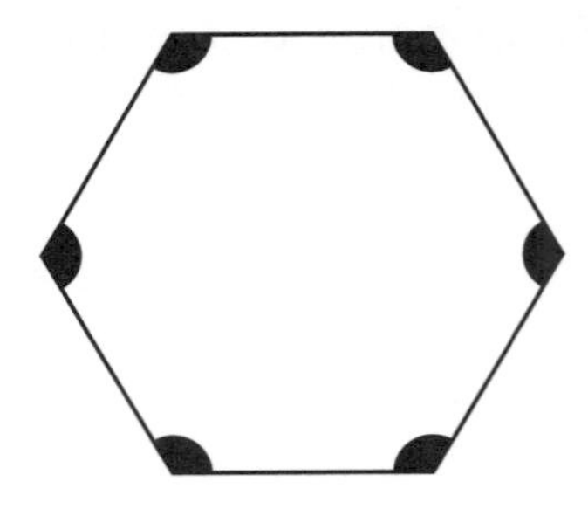

Do not measure with a protractor.

You must show your working.

2

DO NOT WRITE IN THIS MARGIN

Marks

4. The number of peas counted in each of 100 pea pods is shown in this frequency table.

Peas in pod	Frequency	Peas in pod × Frequency
3	5	15
4	10	40
5	28	140
6	36	216
7	12	
8	9	
	Total = 100	Total =

Complete the table above **and** calculate the mean number of peas in a pod.

3

5. Solve algebraically the equation

$$11a - 8 = 37 + 6a.$$

3

[Turn over

DO NOT WRITE IN THIS MARGIN

Marks

6. Anwar wants to buy some accessories for his computer.
He sees this advert for Cathy's Computers.

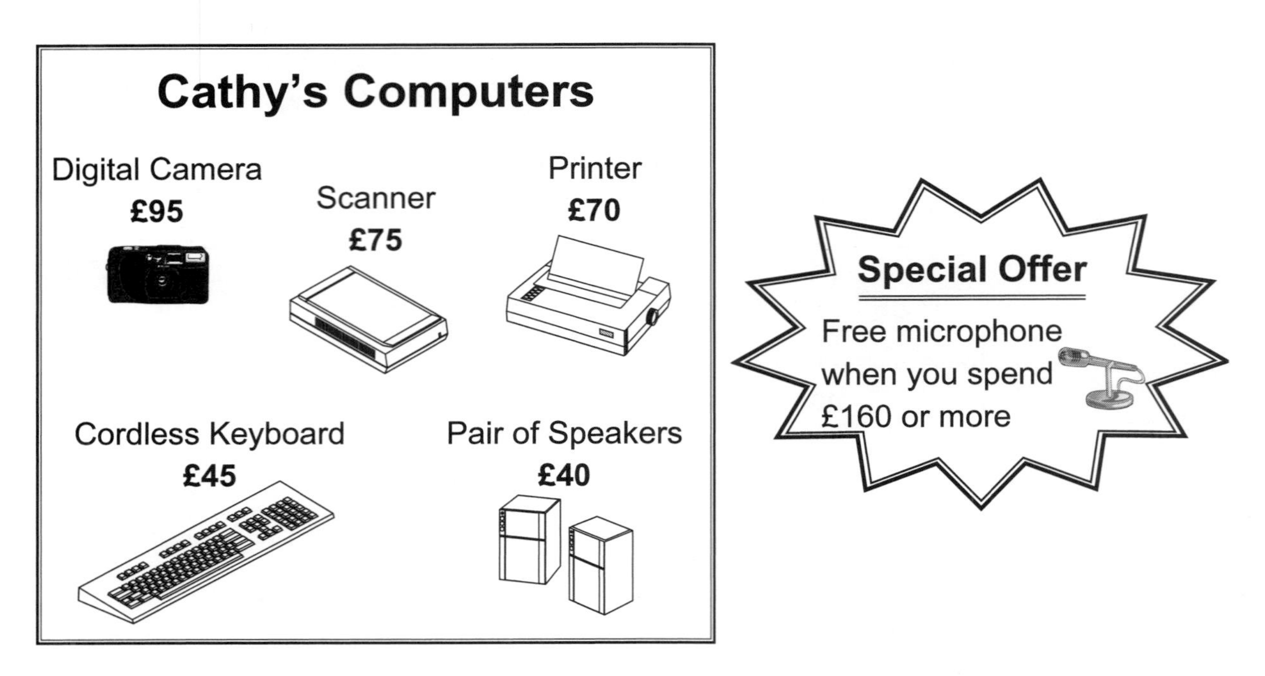

Anwar wants to spend enough to get the free microphone.

He can afford to spend a maximum of £200.

He does not want to buy more than one of each accessory.

One combination of accessories that Anwar can buy is shown in the table below.

Digital Camera £95	Scanner £75	Printer £70	Cordless Keyboard £45	Pair of Speakers £40	Total Value
	✓	✓		✓	£185

Complete the table to show **all** possible combinations that Anwar can buy. **3**

DO NOT WRITE IN THIS MARGIN

Marks

7. (*a*) Complete the table below for $y = -2x + 5$.

x	−2	0	4
y			

2

(*b*) Draw the line $y = -2x + 5$ on the grid.

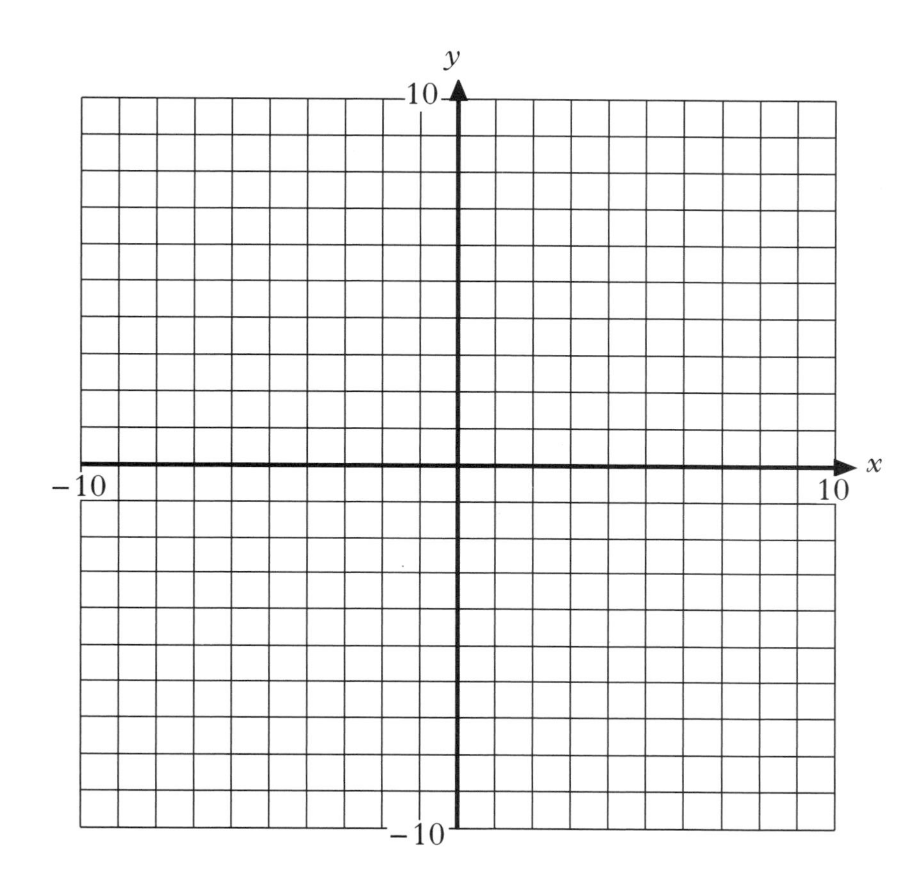

2

[Turn over

DO NOT WRITE IN THIS MARGIN

Marks

8. (*a*) While in New York, Martin changed £50 into US dollars.
The exchange rate was £1 = \$1·62.
How many US dollars did Martin receive for £50? **2**

(*b*) A few days later he received \$320 in exchange for £200.
What was the new exchange rate? **2**

9. (*a*) Write $\frac{7}{1000}$ as a decimal. **1**

(*b*) Starting with the smallest, write the following numbers in order.

$\frac{7}{1000}$, 0·069, $7{\cdot}1 \times 10^{-4}$

Show working to explain your answer. **3**

DO NOT WRITE IN THIS MARGIN

Marks

10. In a **magic square**, the numbers in each row, each column and each diagonal add up to the same **magic total**.

In this magic square the **magic total** is 3.

–2	5	0
3	1	–1
2	–3	4

(*a*)

–4	3	–2
1	–1	–3
0	–5	2

This is another magic square.
What is its **magic total**? **1**

(*b*) Complete this **magic square**.

1		
	–2	
–3		–5

3

[*END OF QUESTION PAPER*]

DO NOT WRITE IN THIS MARGIN

ADDITIONAL SPACE FOR ANSWERS

DO NOT WRITE IN THIS MARGIN

ADDITIONAL SPACE FOR ANSWERS

DO NOT WRITE IN THIS MARGIN

ADDITIONAL SPACE FOR ANSWERS

FOR OFFICIAL USE

Total mark

X100/103

NATIONAL QUALIFICATIONS 2005

FRIDAY, 20 MAY
1.55 PM – 2.50 PM

MATHEMATICS
INTERMEDIATE 1
Units 1, 2 and 3
Paper 2

Fill in these boxes and read what is printed below.

Full name of centre

Town

Forename(s)

Surname

Date of birth
Day Month Year

Scottish candidate number

Number of seat

1 **You may use a calculator.**

2 Write your working and answers in the spaces provided. Additional space is provided at the end of this question-answer book for use if required. If you use this space, write clearly the number of the question involved.

3 Full credit will be given only where the solution contains appropriate working.

4 Before leaving the examination room you must give this book to the invigilator. If you do not you may lose all the marks for this paper.

LIB X100/103 6/11870

FORMULAE LIST

Circumference of a circle: $C = \pi d$

Area of a circle: $A = \pi r^2$

Theorem of Pythagoras:

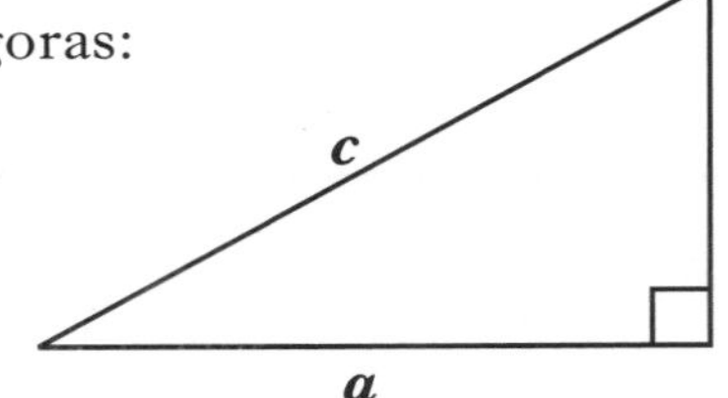

$$a^2 + b^2 = c^2$$

Trigonometric ratios in a right angled triangle:

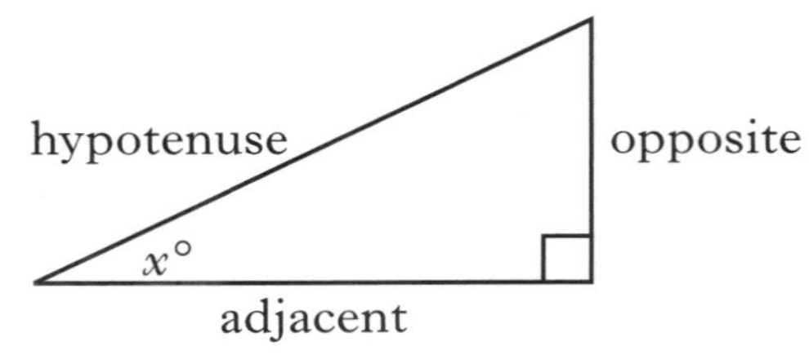

$$\tan x^\circ = \frac{\text{opposite}}{\text{adjacent}}$$

$$\sin x^\circ = \frac{\text{opposite}}{\text{hypotenuse}}$$

$$\cos x^\circ = \frac{\text{adjacent}}{\text{hypotenuse}}$$

DO NOT WRITE IN THIS MARGIN

Marks

ALL questions should be attempted.

1. Calculate the volume of the cube below.

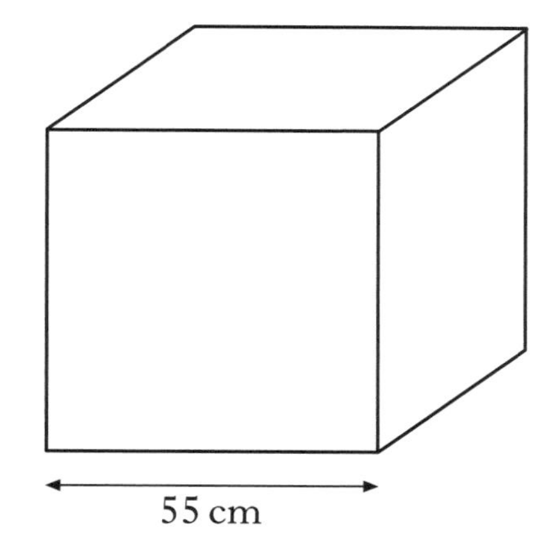

Round your answer to the nearest thousand cubic centimetres. **2**

2. Claire sells cars.
She is paid £250 per month plus 3% commission on her sales.
How much is she paid in a month when her sales are worth £72 000? **2**

[Turn over

DO NOT WRITE IN THIS MARGIN

Marks

3. A group of students visit a theme park.

The graph below shows their journey.

They set off from the college at 9 am and arrive back at 4 pm.

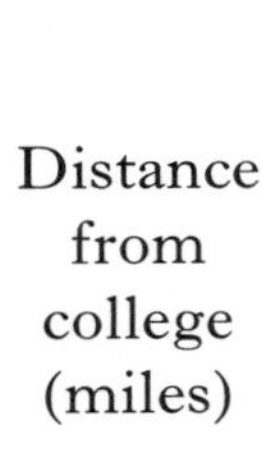

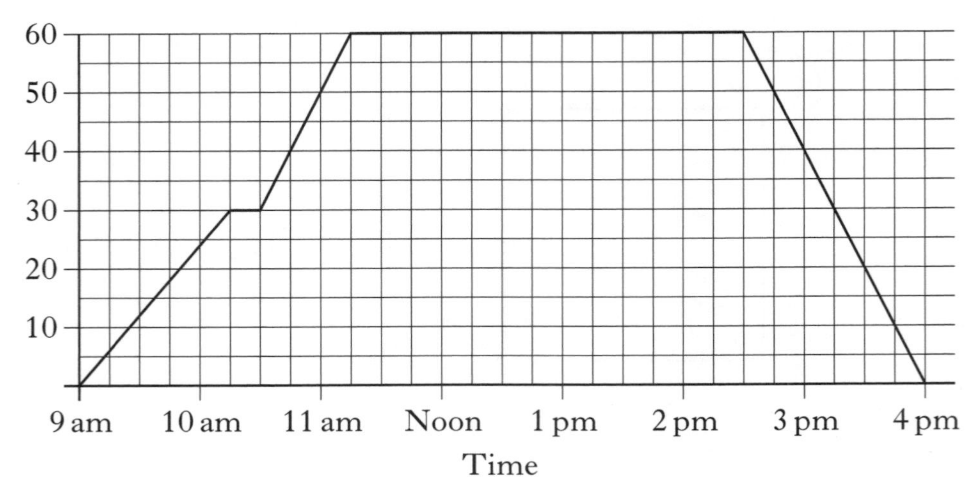

(*a*) How long did the students spend at the theme park? **1**

(*b*) Calculate the average speed, in miles per hour, of the students' return journey. **3**

4. Solve algebraically the inequality

$$3t + 4 > 28.$$

2

DO NOT WRITE IN THIS MARGIN

Marks

5. The stem and leaf diagram below shows the ages of the players in the Kestrels rugby team.

AGES
Kestrels

1	9
2	1 3 4 7 9
3	0 2 4 5 5 5 8 9
4	1

2 | 1 represents 21 years

(*a*) What age is the oldest player? **1**

(*b*) Calculate the range of ages. **2**

The stem and leaf diagram below shows the ages of both the Kestrels and the Falcons rugby teams.

AGES

Falcons		Kestrels
9 9	1	9
8 7 7 6 3 2 1 1 0	2	1 3 4 7 9
8 6 4 3	3	0 2 4 5 5 5 8 9
	4	1

2 | 1 represents 21 years

(*c*) Compare the ages of the two teams. Comment on any difference. **1**

[Turn over

DO NOT WRITE IN THIS MARGIN

Marks

6. (*a*) Multiply out the brackets and simplify

$$11n + 4(7 - 2n).$$

2

(*b*) Factorise $15 + 6x$.

2

7. The scores of 12 golfers in a competition were as follows.

67	70	68	75	71	70
70	75	76	75	74	75

(*a*) Find the modal score.

1

(*b*) Find the median score.

2

(*c*) Find the probability of choosing a golfer from this group with a score of 70.

1

DO NOT WRITE IN THIS MARGIN

Marks

8. 60 workers in a factory voted on a new pay deal.
42 of them voted to accept the deal.
What percentage voted to accept the deal?

3

9. The pie chart shows the different sizes of eggs laid by a flock of hens.

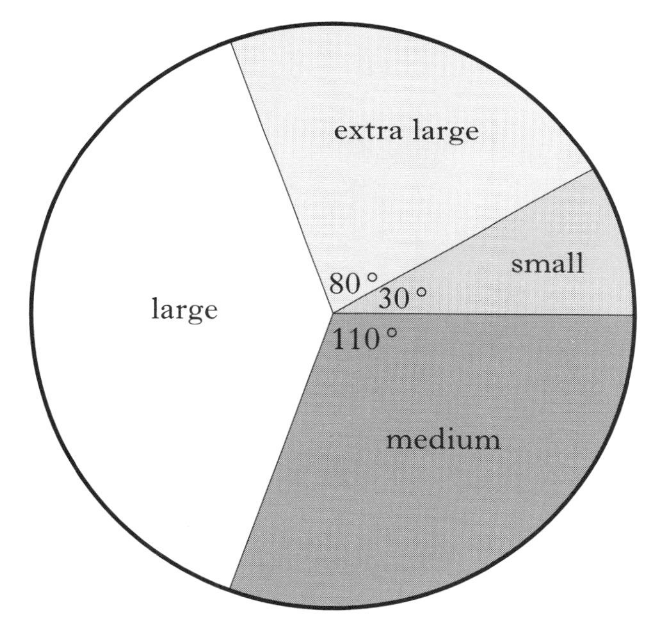

The flock of hens laid 1260 eggs.
How many of the eggs were large?

3

[Turn over

Marks

10. A rectangular shelf is supported by brackets as shown.
Each bracket is a right angled triangle.

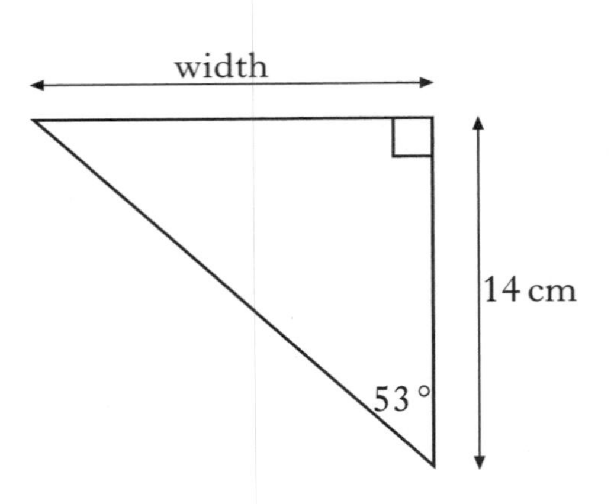

Calculate the width of this bracket.
Give your answer correct to one decimal place.
Do not use a scale drawing.

4

DO NOT WRITE IN THIS MARGIN

Marks

11. The diagram below shows a speedway track.

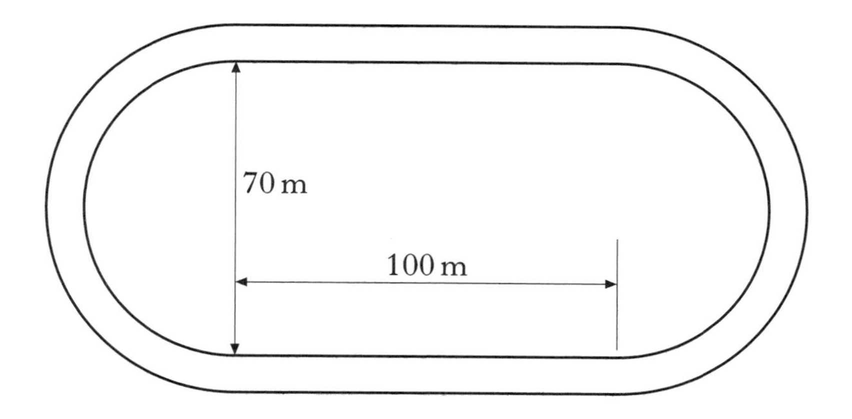

The straights are each 100 metres long.

The bends are semi-circles as shown.

Calculate the perimeter of the inside of the track. **4**

12. Use the formula below to find the value of A when $b = 2{\cdot}4$ and $c = 5$.

$$A = 3bc^2$$

3

[Turn over

DO NOT WRITE IN THIS MARGIN

Marks

13. PQRS is a rhombus.

The diagonals PR and QS are 15 centimetres and 8 centimetres long as shown.

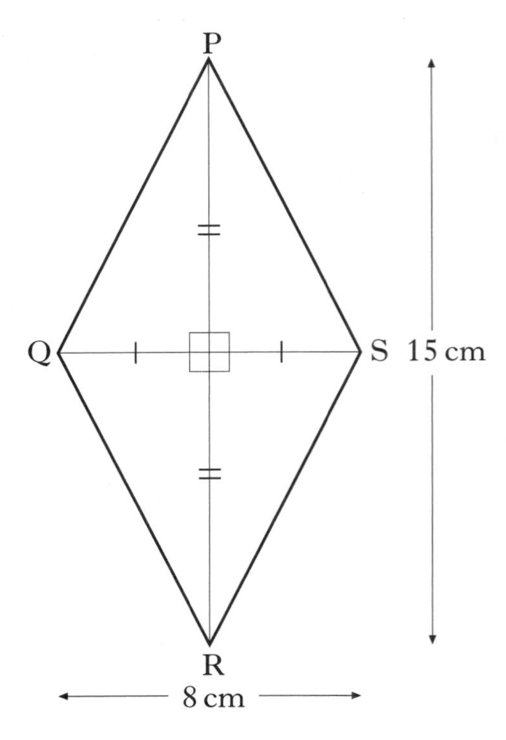

Calculate the length of side PQ.

Do not use a scale drawing.

3

14. Margaret is recovering from an operation.

She needs to take 4 tablets each day for a year.

The tablets are supplied in boxes of 200.

Each box costs £6·50.

How much does it cost for the year's supply?

3

DO NOT WRITE IN THIS MARGIN

Marks

15. The diagram below shows a plan of a patio.

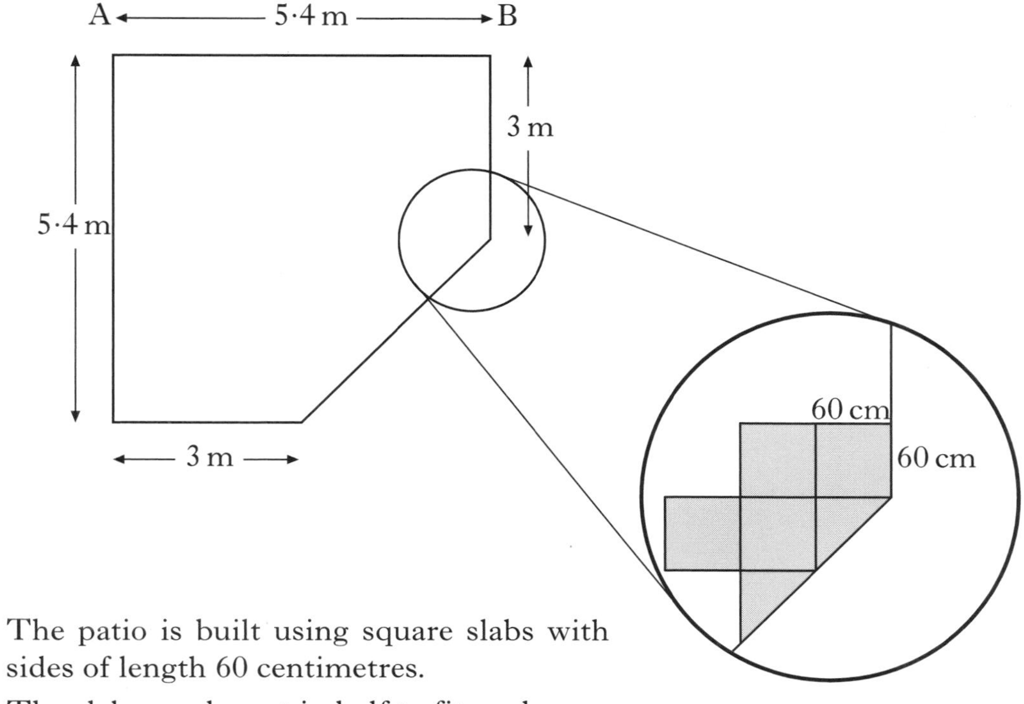

The patio is built using square slabs with sides of length 60 centimetres.

The slabs can be cut in half to fit as shown.

(*a*) How many slabs fit exactly along edge AB? **1**

(*b*) How many slabs are needed altogether to build the patio? **4**

[*END OF QUESTION PAPER*]

ADDITIONAL SPACE FOR ANSWERS

2006 | Intermediate I

[BLANK PAGE]

FOR OFFICIAL USE

Total mark

X100/101

NATIONAL QUALIFICATIONS 2006

FRIDAY, 19 MAY
1.00 PM – 1.35 PM

MATHEMATICS
INTERMEDIATE 1
Units 1, 2 and 3
Paper 1
(Non-calculator)

Fill in these boxes and read what is printed below.

Full name of centre

Town

Forename(s)

Surname

Date of birth
Day Month Year

Scottish candidate number

Number of seat

1 **You may NOT use a calculator.**

2 Write your working and answers in the spaces provided. Additional space is provided at the end of this question-answer book for use if required. If you use this space, write clearly the number of the question involved.

3 Full credit will be given only where the solution contains appropriate working.

4 Before leaving the examination room you must give this book to the invigilator. If you do not you may lose all the marks for this paper.

LI X100/101 6/12870

FORMULAE LIST

Circumference of a circle: $C = \pi d$

Area of a circle: $A = \pi r^2$

Theorem of Pythagoras:

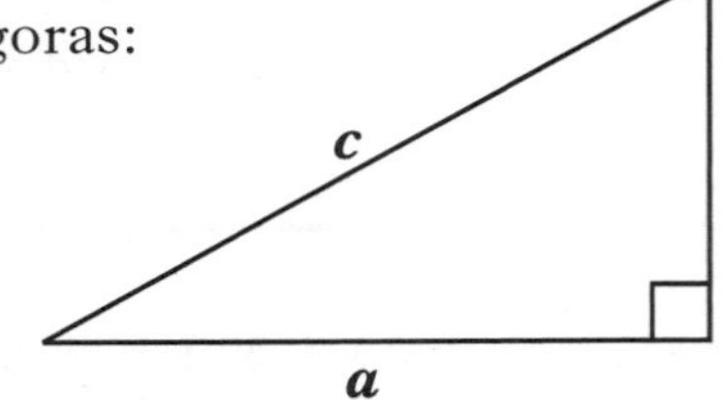

$a^2 + b^2 = c^2$

Trigonometric ratios in a right angled triangle:

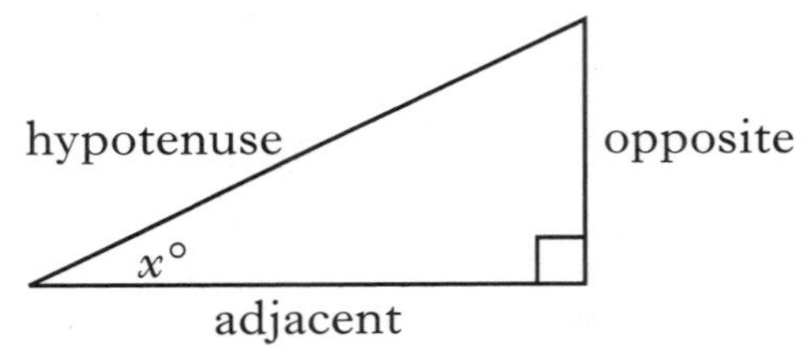

$$\tan x° = \frac{\text{opposite}}{\text{adjacent}}$$

$$\sin x° = \frac{\text{opposite}}{\text{hypotenuse}}$$

$$\cos x° = \frac{\text{adjacent}}{\text{hypotenuse}}$$

DO NOT WRITE IN THIS MARGIN

Marks

ALL questions should be attempted.

1. Find 5·42 – 1·8. **1**

2. A tree surgeon uses this rule to work out his charge in pounds for uprooting and removing trees.

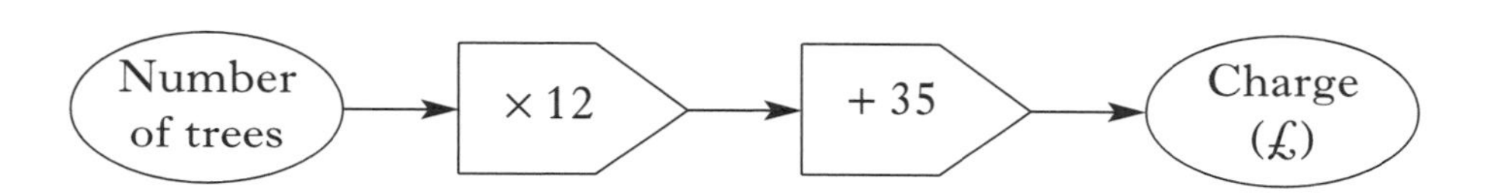

How much would he charge to uproot and remove 11 trees? **2**

[Turn over

DO NOT WRITE IN THIS MARGIN

Marks

3. Paula runs a 1500 metre race at an average speed of 6 metres per second.

How long does she take to run the race?

Give her time in minutes and seconds.

3

4. The table below shows insurance premiums for holidays abroad.

	INSURANCE PREMIUM per adult		
	Europe	Worldwide	Winter Sports
Up to 8 days	£15	£30	£40
9–17 days	£20	£40	£55
18–26 days	£30	£60	£80

Child premium (0–15 years) is 70% of the adult premium.

Mr and Mrs Fleming and their 5 year old son go to the USA for a three week holiday in July.

Find the **total** insurance premium for the family.

3

DO NOT WRITE IN THIS MARGIN

Marks

5. The hire purchase price of this camcorder is £499.

How much will each payment be? **3**

6. Solve algebraically the equation

$$5n + 9 = 51 - 2n.$$

3

[Turn over

DO NOT WRITE IN THIS MARGIN

Marks

7. (*a*) Complete the table below for $y = 2 + 3x$.

x	-3	0	2
y			

2

(*b*) Draw the line $y = 2 + 3x$ on the grid.

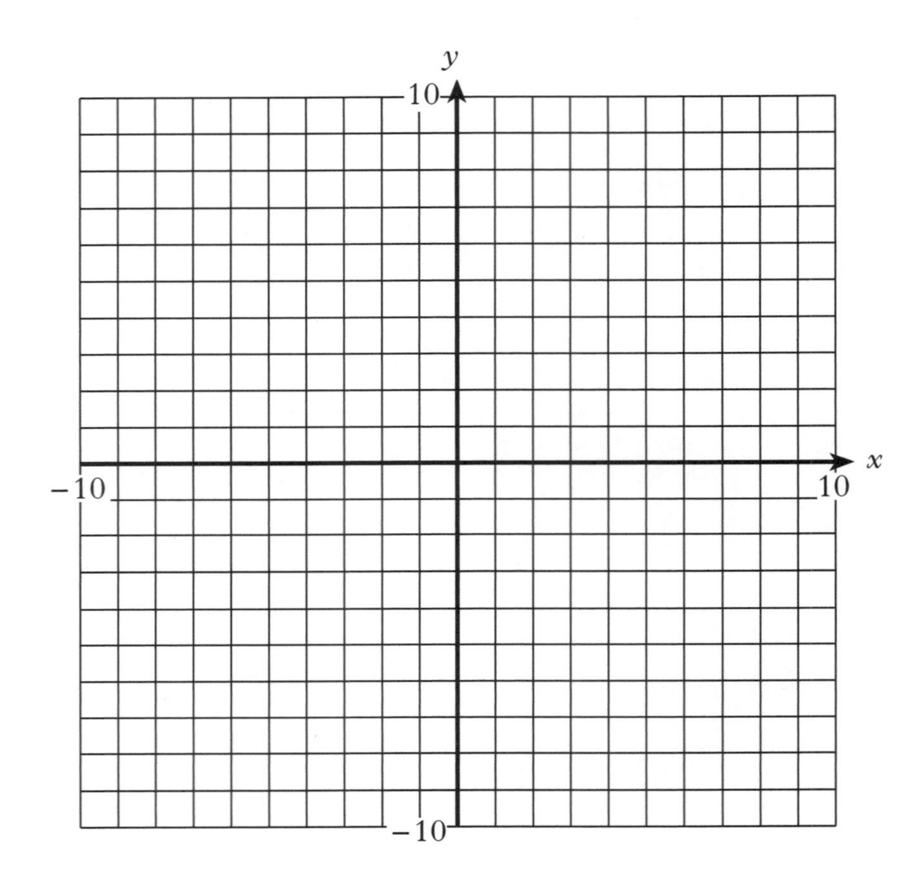

2

DO NOT WRITE IN THIS MARGIN

Marks

8. A television programme has a phone-in to raise money for charity.

The calls cost 70 pence per minute.

The charity receives $\frac{3}{5}$ of the cost of each call.

How much money will the charity receive from a call which lasts $2\frac{1}{2}$ minutes?

3

9. Use the formula below to find the value of I when $P = 144$ and $R = 4$.

$$I = \sqrt{\frac{P}{R}}$$

3

[Turn over for Question 10 on *Page eight*

DO NOT WRITE IN THIS MARGIN

Marks

10. This is a number cell.

1st	2nd	3rd	4th
3	−2	1	−1

- 1st number + 2nd number = 3rd number $3 + (-2) = 1$
- 2nd number + 3rd number = 4th number $(-2) + 1 = -1$

(*a*) Complete this number cell.

4	−6		

1

(*b*) Complete this number cell.

		−1	4

2

(*c*) Complete this number cell.

1			−7

2

YOU MAY USE THE BLANK NUMBER CELLS BELOW FOR WORKING IF YOU WISH.

[*END OF QUESTION PAPER*]

ADDITIONAL SPACE FOR ANSWERS

DO NOT WRITE IN THIS MARGIN

ADDITIONAL SPACE FOR ANSWERS

DO NOT WRITE IN THIS MARGIN

ADDITIONAL SPACE FOR ANSWERS

[BLANK PAGE]

FOR OFFICIAL USE

Total mark

X100/103

NATIONAL QUALIFICATIONS 2006

FRIDAY, 19 MAY
1.55 PM – 2.50 PM

MATHEMATICS
INTERMEDIATE 1
Units 1, 2 and 3
Paper 2

Fill in these boxes and read what is printed below.

Full name of centre

Town

Forename(s)

Surname

Date of birth
Day Month Year

Scottish candidate number

Number of seat

1 **You may use a calculator.**

2 Write your working and answers in the spaces provided. Additional space is provided at the end of this question-answer book for use if required. If you use this space, write clearly the number of the question involved.

3 Full credit will be given only where the solution contains appropriate working.

4 Before leaving the examination room you must give this book to the invigilator. If you do not you may lose all the marks for this paper.

LI X100/103 6/12870

FORMULAE LIST

Circumference of a circle: $C = \pi d$

Area of a circle: $A = \pi r^2$

Theorem of Pythagoras:

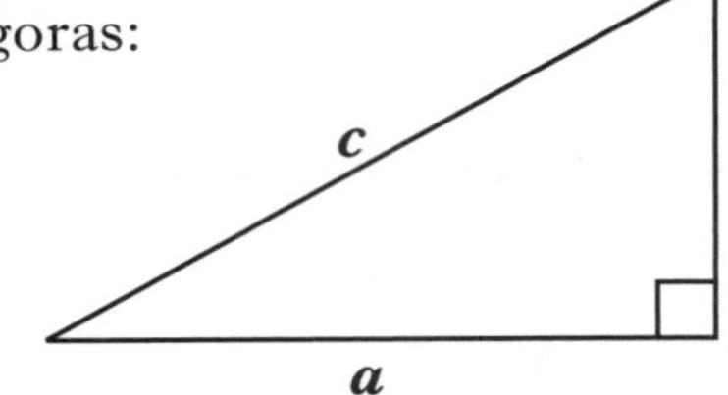

$a^2 + b^2 = c^2$

Trigonometric ratios in a right angled triangle:

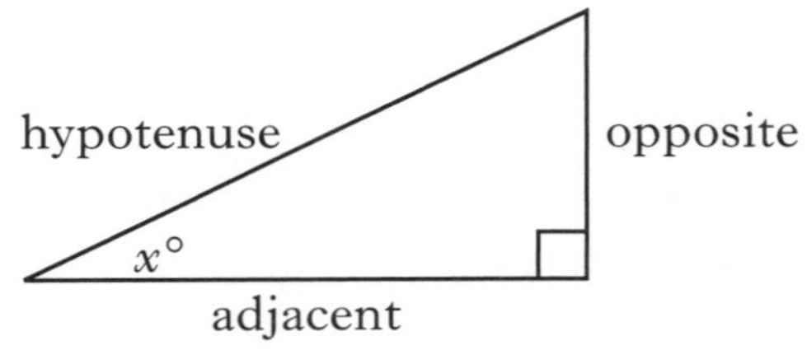

$$\tan x° = \frac{\textbf{opposite}}{\textbf{adjacent}}$$

$$\sin x° = \frac{\textbf{opposite}}{\textbf{hypotenuse}}$$

$$\cos x° = \frac{\textbf{adjacent}}{\textbf{hypotenuse}}$$

DO NOT WRITE IN THIS MARGIN

Marks

ALL questions should be attempted.

1. During a holiday in Mexico, Lee changed £650 into pesos.

The exchange rate was £1 = 19·13 pesos.

How many pesos did Lee receive for £650?

Round off your answer to the nearest ten pesos. **2**

2. Light travels one mile in about 0·000 005 4 seconds.

Write this time in standard form. **2**

[Turn over

DO NOT WRITE IN THIS MARGIN

Marks

3. Solve algebraically the inequality

$$4t - 7 > 29.$$

2

4. The number of bricks needed to build a wall is proportional to the area of the wall.

A wall with an area of 4 square metres needs 260 bricks.

How many bricks are needed for a wall with an area of 7 square metres?

2

DO NOT WRITE IN THIS MARGIN

Marks

5. A group of 40 students sit a test.

The marks scored by the students in the test are shown in the frequency table below.

Mark	*Frequency*
14	6
15	10
16	7
17	7
18	5
19	3
20	2

(*a*) Write down the modal mark. **1**

(*b*) Find the probability of choosing a student from this group with a mark of 19. **1**

(*c*) Complete the table below and calculate the mean mark for the group.

Mark	*Frequency*	*Mark* x *Frequency*
14	6	84
15	10	150
16	7	112
17	7	119
18	5	
19	3	
20	2	
	Total = 40	Total =

3

DO NOT WRITE IN THIS MARGIN

Marks

6. A water tank is 50 centimetres wide, 1·2 metres long and 40 centimetres high. Calculate its volume.

Give your answer in litres.
(1 litre = 1000 cubic centimetres.)

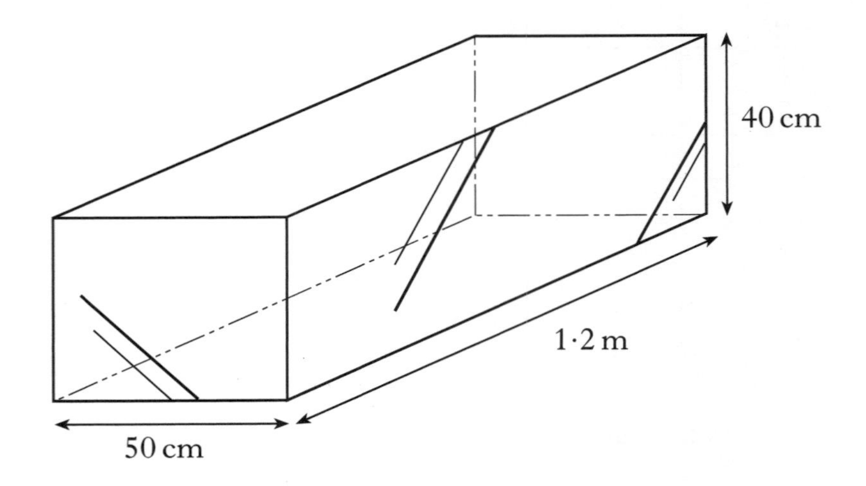

3

7. (*a*) Multiply out the brackets and simplify

$$3y + 2(x - 4y).$$

2

(*b*) Factorise $8d + 12$.

2

Marks

8. Every morning for one week, Wellburgh Council carried out a traffic survey at a busy junction.

The number of cars waiting to turn right at the junction was counted every five minutes between 8 am and 9 am.

On Monday morning the results were:

10 14 17 12 14 11 13 7 8 7 6 2.

Calculate:

(*a*) the median; **2**

(*b*) the range. **2**

On Saturday morning, the median was 6 and the range was 8.

(*c*) Make **two** comments comparing the number of cars waiting to turn right at the junction on Monday morning and Saturday morning. **2**

[Turn over

DO NOT WRITE IN THIS MARGIN

Marks

9. Stephen is playing snooker.

The diagram below shows the positions of three balls on the table.

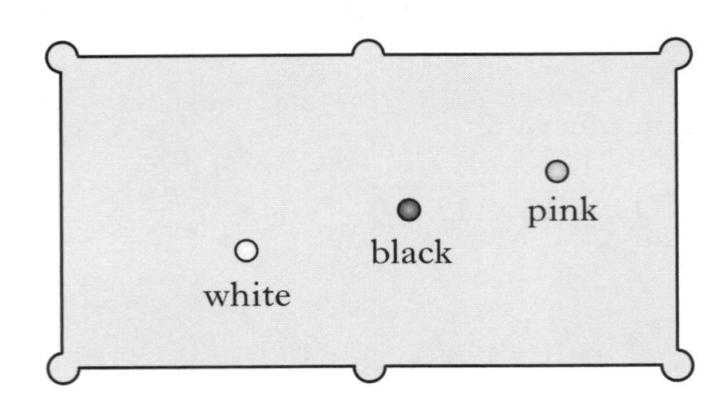

Stephen plays the white ball, W.

It bounces off the side of the table at X and hits the pink ball, P.

- Distance WX is 1·1 metres
- Distance XP is 0·7 metres
- Angle WXP is 90 °

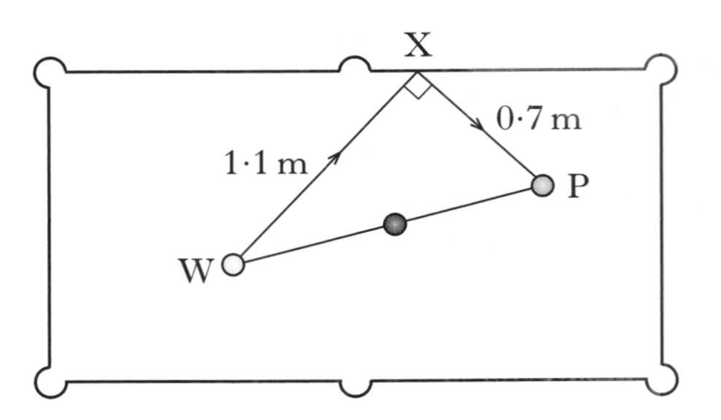

Calculate distance WP.

Do not use a scale drawing.

3

DO NOT WRITE IN THIS MARGIN

Marks

10. The table below shows the stopping distances of a car, when the brakes are applied, at different speeds.

Speed (miles per hour)	0	10	20	30	40
Stopping distance (feet)	0	15	40	75	120

On the grid below, draw a **line** graph to show this information.

4

[Turn over

DO NOT WRITE IN THIS MARGIN

Marks

11. Ralph invests £2600 in a building society account.

The rate of interest is 4·5% per annum.

Calculate the interest he should receive after 8 months.

3

DO NOT WRITE IN THIS MARGIN

Marks

12. A road bridge can be raised in the **centre** to allow ships to pass through.

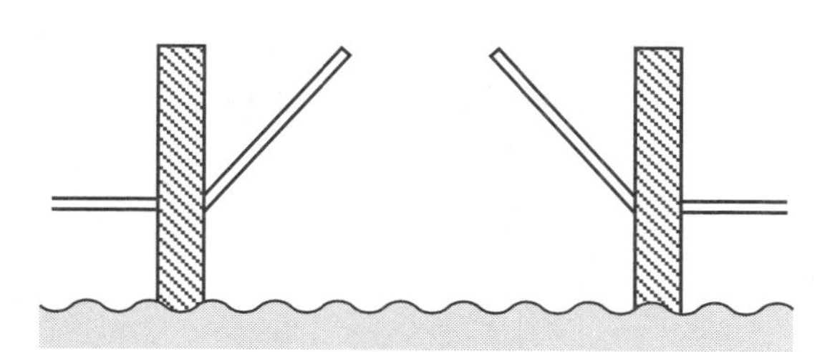

The moveable sections of the bridge are:

- 10 metres above the water level
- 40 metres long altogether.

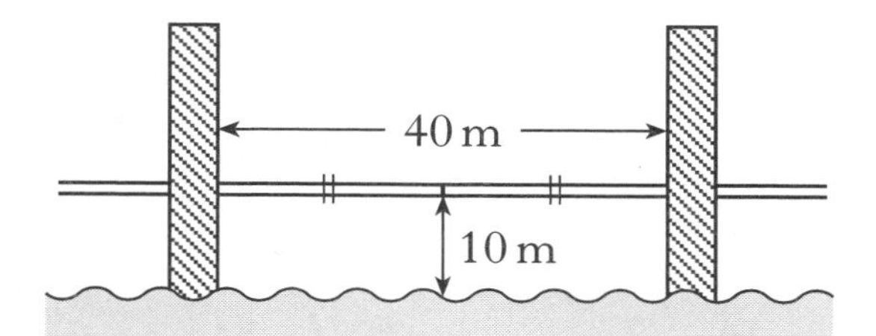

The moveable sections are raised through 50 ° to allow a ship to pass through.

Calculate the height of the point P above the water level.

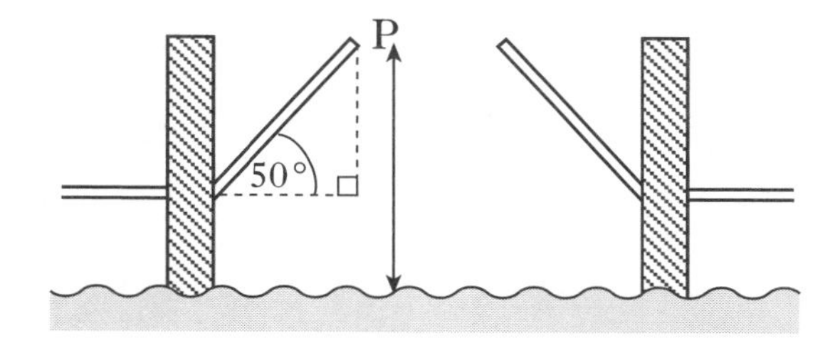

Do not use a scale drawing.

5

[Turn over

DO NOT WRITE IN THIS MARGIN

Marks

13. Andrew designs a website to advertise his hotel.

In the first month he has 250 visitors to his site.

The following month he has 300 visitors.

Calculate the percentage increase in the number of visitors.

4

DO NOT WRITE IN THIS MARGIN

Marks

14. The diagram below shows the wall at the start of a tunnel.

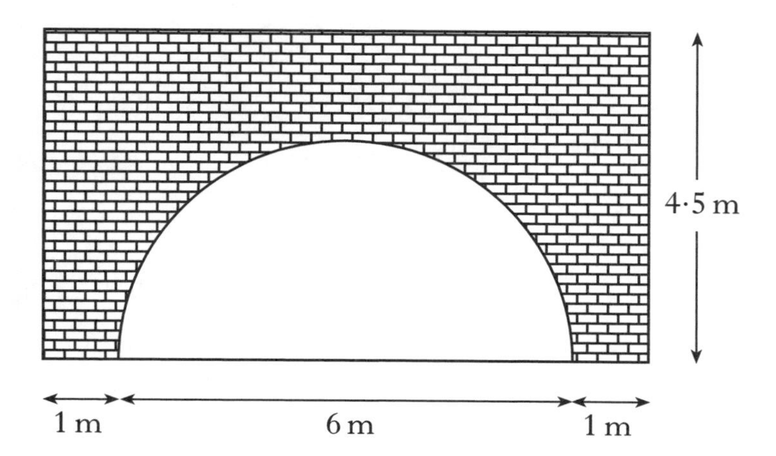

The wall is in the shape of a rectangle with a semi-circular space for the tunnel.

Calculate the area of the wall in square metres.

Give your answer correct to one decimal place.

5

[*END OF QUESTION PAPER*]

DO NOT WRITE IN THIS MARGIN

ADDITIONAL SPACE FOR ANSWERS

2007 | Intermediate I

[BLANK PAGE]

FOR OFFICIAL USE

Total mark

X100/101

NATIONAL QUALIFICATIONS 2007

TUESDAY, 15 MAY
1.00 PM – 1.35 PM

MATHEMATICS
INTERMEDIATE 1
Units 1, 2 and 3
Paper 1
(Non-calculator)

Fill in these boxes and read what is printed below.

Full name of centre

Town

Forename(s)

Surname

Date of birth
Day Month Year

Scottish candidate number

Number of seat

1 **You may NOT use a calculator.**

2 Write your working and answers in the spaces provided. Additional space is provided at the end of this question-answer book for use if required. If you use this space, write clearly the number of the question involved.

3 Full credit will be given only where the solution contains appropriate working.

4 Before leaving the examination room you must give this book to the invigilator. If you do not you may lose all the marks for this paper.

LI X100/101 6/21770

FORMULAE LIST

Circumference of a circle: $C = \pi d$

Area of a circle: $A = \pi r^2$

Theorem of Pythagoras:

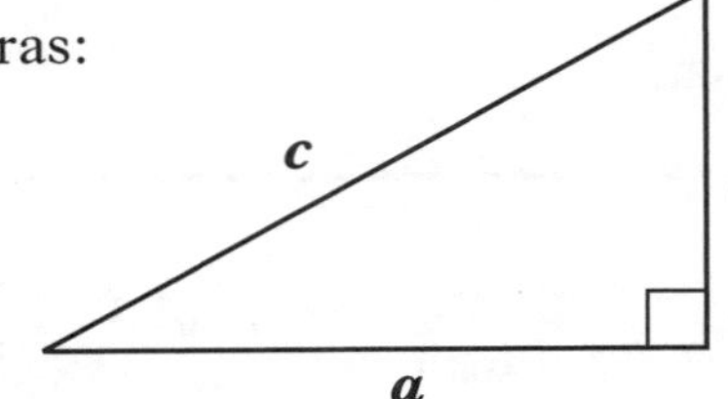

$$a^2 + b^2 = c^2$$

Trigonometric ratios in a right angled triangle:

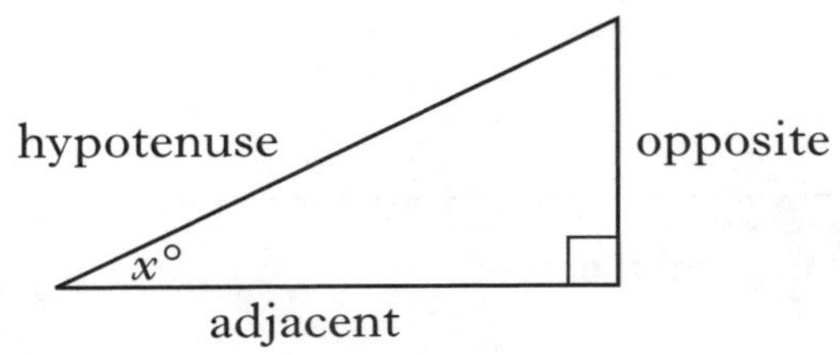

$$\tan x^\circ = \frac{\text{opposite}}{\text{adjacent}}$$

$$\sin x^\circ = \frac{\text{opposite}}{\text{hypotenuse}}$$

$$\cos x^\circ = \frac{\text{adjacent}}{\text{hypotenuse}}$$

DO NOT WRITE IN THIS MARGIN

Marks

ALL questions should be attempted.

1. (*a*) Find 8·52 + 10·7. **1**

(*b*) Find 3·76 ÷ 8. **1**

(*c*) Change 0·057 into a fraction. **1**

(*d*) Find 90% of £320. **2**

2. Shona wants to insure her jewellery for £8000.

The insurance company charges an annual premium of £7·65 for each £1000 insured.

Work out Shona's annual premium. **2**

DO NOT WRITE IN THIS MARGIN

Marks

3. Solve algebraically the inequality

$$7a + 6 < 69.$$

2

4. The number of minutes that patients had to sit in the waiting room before seeing their doctor was recorded one day.

The results are shown in the frequency table below.

Number of minutes	Frequency	Number of minutes × Frequency
5	4	20
6	7	42
7	8	56
8	13	104
9	12	
10	6	
	Total = 50	Total =

Complete the table above **and** find the mean number of minutes.

3

DO NOT WRITE IN THIS MARGIN

Marks

5. (*a*) Complete the table below for $y = 4x - 3$.

x	–1	0	1	3
y			1	

2

(*b*) Draw the line $y = 4x - 3$ on the grid.

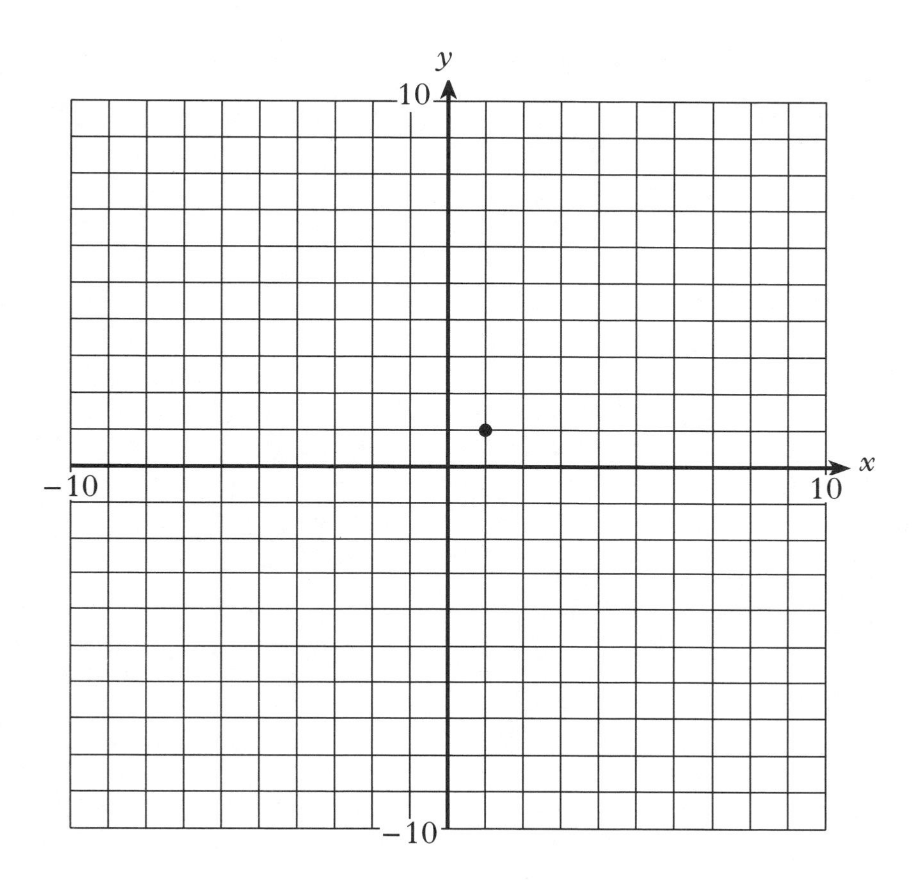

2

[Turn over

DO NOT WRITE IN THIS MARGIN

Marks

6. Shown below is a container in the shape of a cuboid.

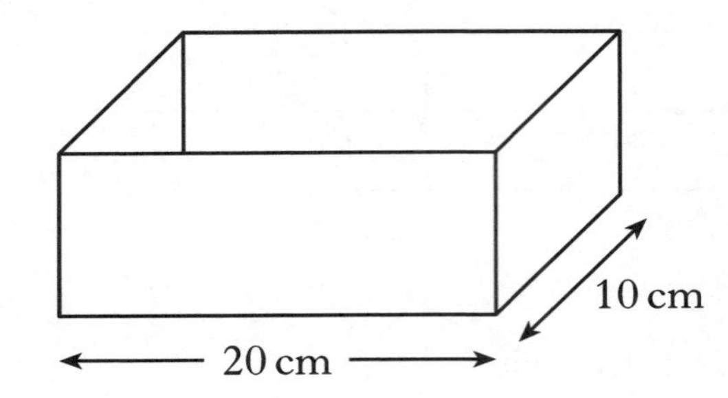

When full, the container holds 1600 cubic centimetres of water.

Work out the height of the container. **3**

7. Work out the answers to the following.

(*a*) $2 \times (-2) \times 2$ **1**

(*b*) $11 - (-6)$ **1**

DO NOT WRITE IN THIS MARGIN

Marks

8. Naveed has six electrical appliances in his student lodgings.

The power, in watts, used by each appliance is shown below.

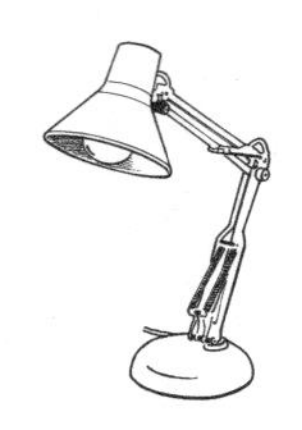

Lamp 100 watts

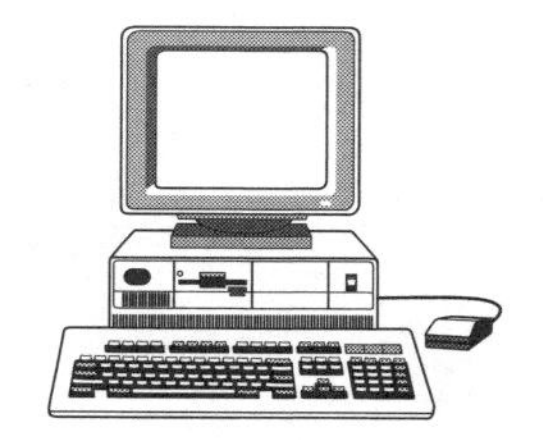

Computer 200 watts

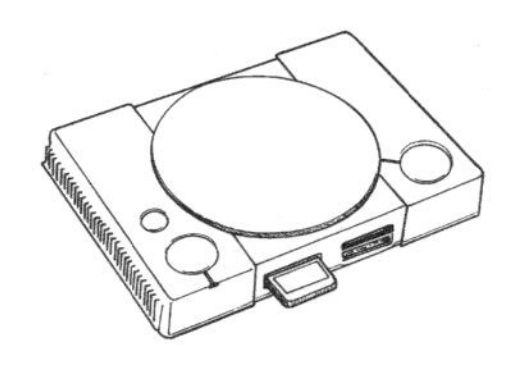

Games Machine 400 watts

Microwave 700 watts

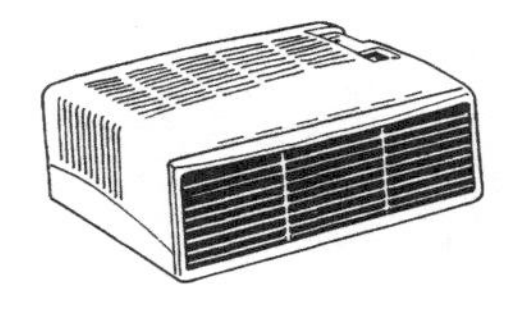

Heater 1000 watts

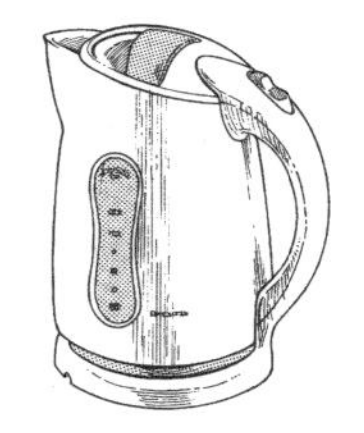

Kettle 2300 watts

Naveed uses a 4-way extension lead for the appliances.

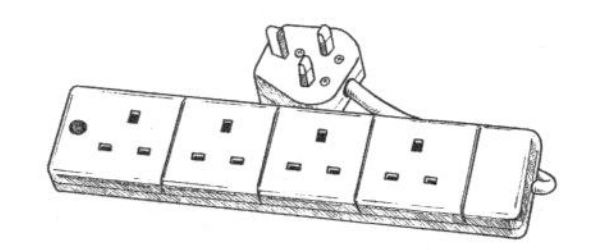

The instructions state that the maximum power used through the extension lead should not be more than 3000 watts.

One combination of **four** appliances that Naveed can safely use through the extension lead is shown in the table below.

Lamp 100 watts	*Computer* 200 watts	*Games Machine* 400 watts	*Microwave* 700 watts	*Heater* 1000 watts	*Kettle* 2300 watts	*Total Watts*
✓	✓	✓		✓		1700

Complete the table to show **all** the possible combinations of **four** appliances that Naveed can safely use through the extension lead. **3**

[Turn over for Questions 9 and 10 on *Page eight*

DO NOT WRITE IN THIS MARGIN

Marks

9. The formula for the area of a trapezium is

$$A = \frac{1}{2}h(a + b)$$

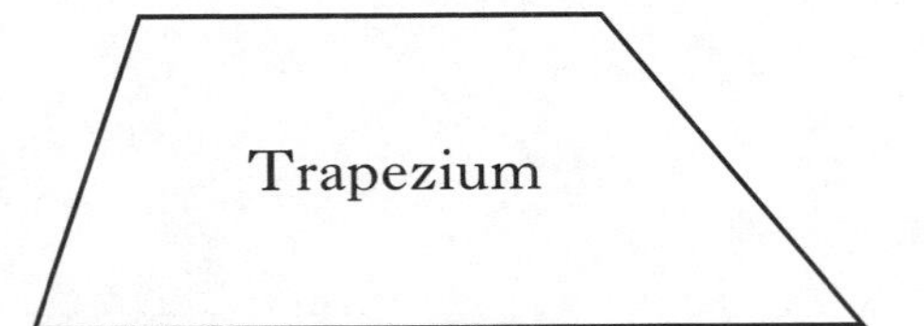

Find A when $a = 11$, $b = 7$ and $h = 6$. **3**

10. Black and white counters are placed in two bags as shown below.

Bag 1

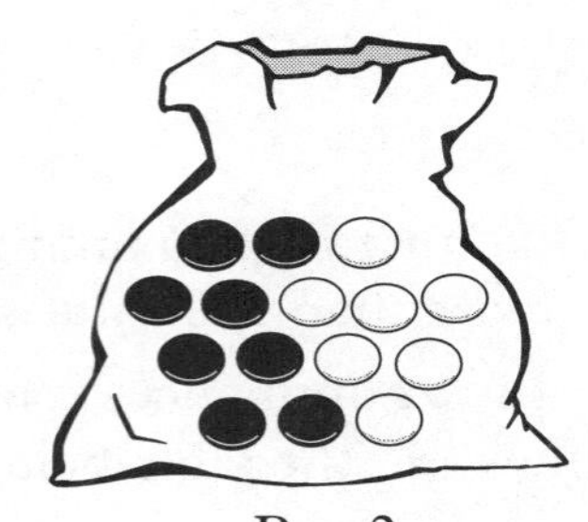
Bag 2

One counter is selected at random from **each** bag.
Which bag gives a greater probability of selecting a black counter?
Explain your answer. **3**

[END OF QUESTION PAPER]

DO NOT WRITE IN THIS MARGIN

ADDITIONAL SPACE FOR ANSWERS

DO NOT WRITE IN THIS MARGIN

ADDITIONAL SPACE FOR ANSWERS

DO NOT WRITE IN THIS MARGIN

ADDITIONAL SPACE FOR ANSWERS

[BLANK PAGE]

FOR OFFICIAL USE

Total mark

X100/103

NATIONAL QUALIFICATIONS 2007

TUESDAY, 15 MAY
1.55 PM – 2.50 PM

MATHEMATICS
INTERMEDIATE 1
Units 1, 2 and 3
Paper 2

Fill in these boxes and read what is printed below.

Full name of centre

Town

Forename(s)

Surname

Date of birth
Day Month Year

Scottish candidate number

Number of seat

1 **You may use a calculator.**

2 Write your working and answers in the spaces provided. Additional space is provided at the end of this question-answer book for use if required. If you use this space, write clearly the number of the question involved.

3 Full credit will be given only where the solution contains appropriate working.

4 Before leaving the examination room you must give this book to the invigilator. If you do not you may lose all the marks for this paper.

FORMULAE LIST

Circumference of a circle: $C = \pi d$

Area of a circle: $A = \pi r^2$

Theorem of Pythagoras:

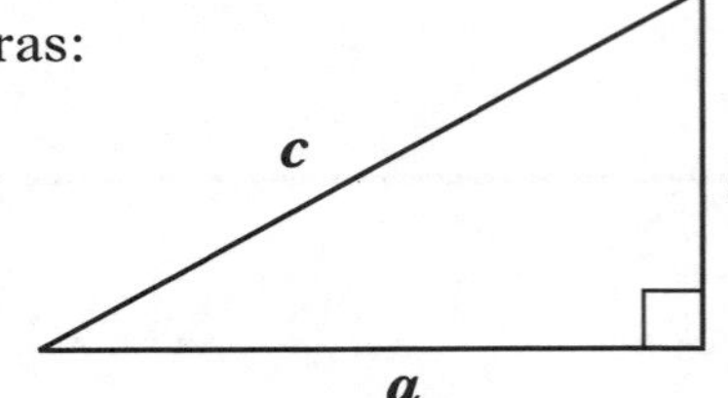

$a^2 + b^2 = c^2$

Trigonometric ratios in a right angled triangle:

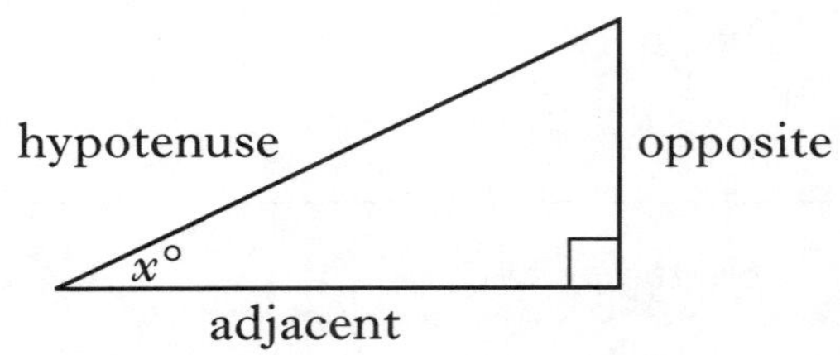

$$\tan x^\circ = \frac{\text{opposite}}{\text{adjacent}}$$

$$\sin x^\circ = \frac{\text{opposite}}{\text{hypotenuse}}$$

$$\cos x^\circ = \frac{\text{adjacent}}{\text{hypotenuse}}$$

DO NOT WRITE IN THIS MARGIN

Marks

ALL questions should be attempted.

1. The bar graph shows the number of hotels in Southbay awarded grades A to E by the local tourist board.

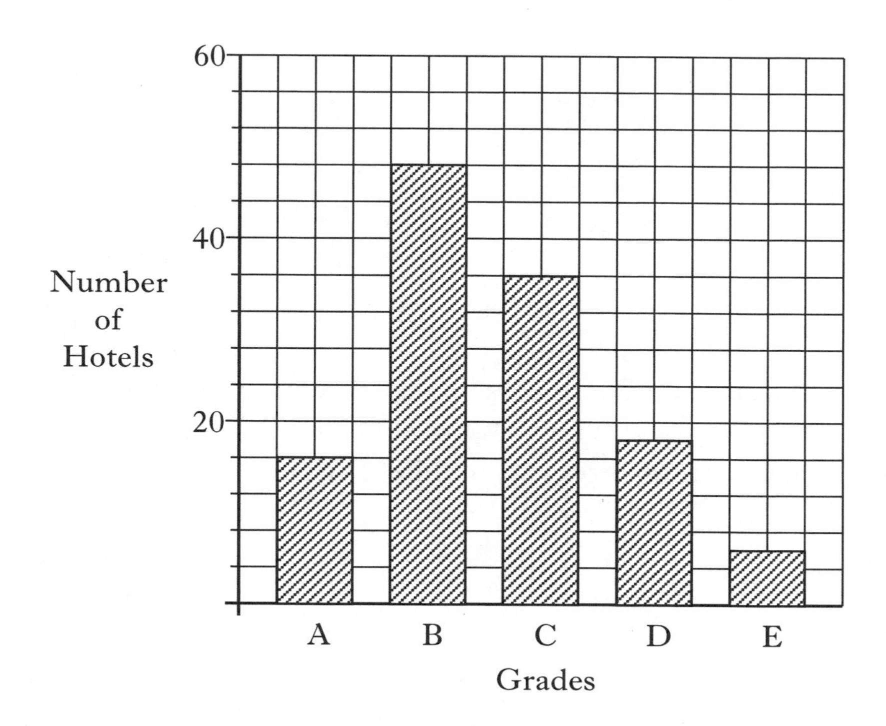

(*a*) How many hotels were awarded an A grade? **1**

(*b*) Write down the modal grade. **1**

[Turn over

DO NOT WRITE IN THIS MARGIN

Marks

2. The distance from Earth to the Sun is approximately 150 million kilometres. Write this number in standard form.

2

3. An aeroplane took off from Edinburgh at 0753 and landed in Shetland at 0908. The distance flown by the aeroplane was 295 miles.

Calculate the average speed of the aeroplane in miles per hour.

3

4. Solve algebraically the equation

$$17y - 12 = 3y + 44.$$

3

DO NOT WRITE IN THIS MARGIN

Marks

5. A teacher records the number of absences and end of term test mark for each of her students.

The scattergraph shows the results.

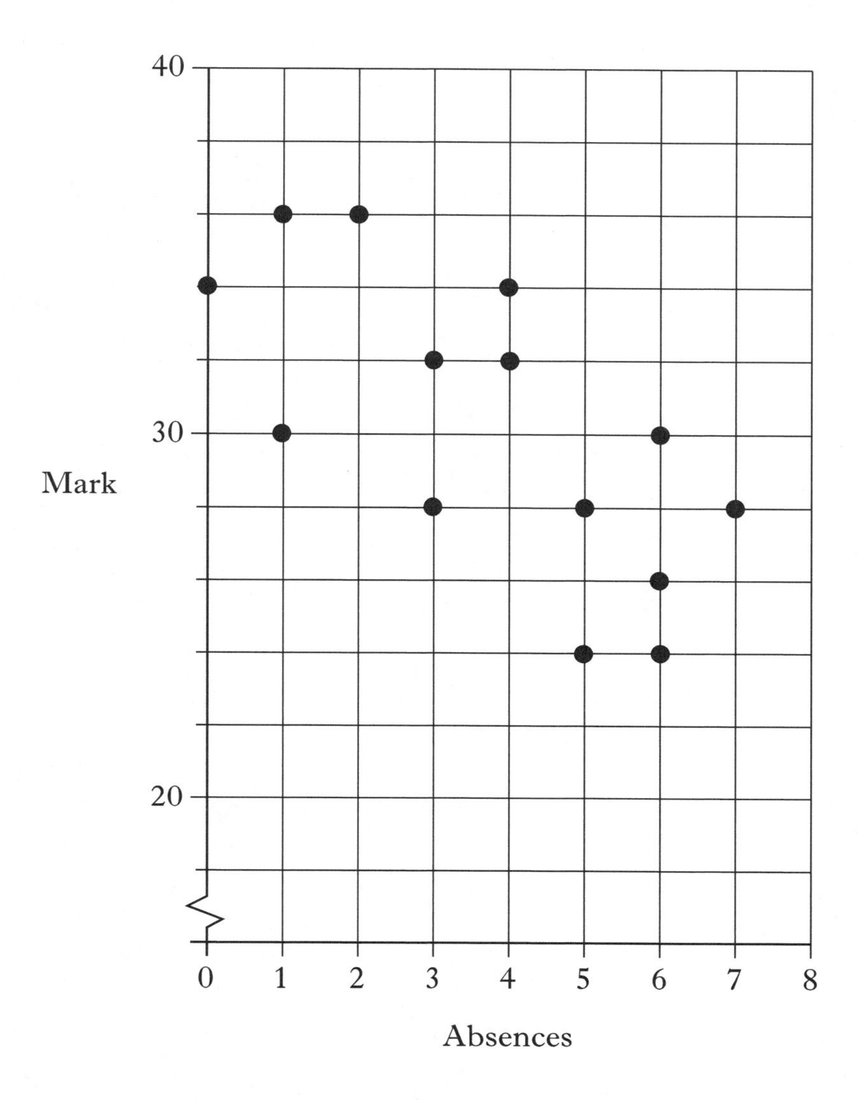

(*a*) Draw a line of best fit through the points on the graph. **1**

(*b*) Use your line of best fit to estimate the mark of a student who had 8 absences. **1**

[Turn over

DO NOT WRITE IN THIS MARGIN

Marks

6. (*a*) Multiply out the brackets and simplify

$$3(5p + 3) - 2p.$$

2

(*b*) Factorise $21 - 14m$.

2

Marks

7. The weights of two groups of ten people are to be compared.
Listed below are the weights (in kilograms) of the ten people in group A.

64 71 73 66 69 78 77 75 76 71

(*a*) Find the median. **2**

(*b*) Find the range. **2**

(*c*) For the ten people in group B the median is 76 and the range is 20.
Make **two** comments comparing the weights of the people in group A and group B. **2**

[Turn over

DO NOT WRITE IN THIS MARGIN

Marks

8. Sam invests £7600 in a bank account.

- The rate of interest is 4·8% per annum.
- The bank deducts 20% tax from the interest.

Calculate the interest Sam receives for one year after tax has been deducted.

3

DO NOT WRITE IN THIS MARGIN

Marks

9. Phil is making a wooden bed frame.

The frame is rectangular and measures 195 centimetres by 95 centimetres.

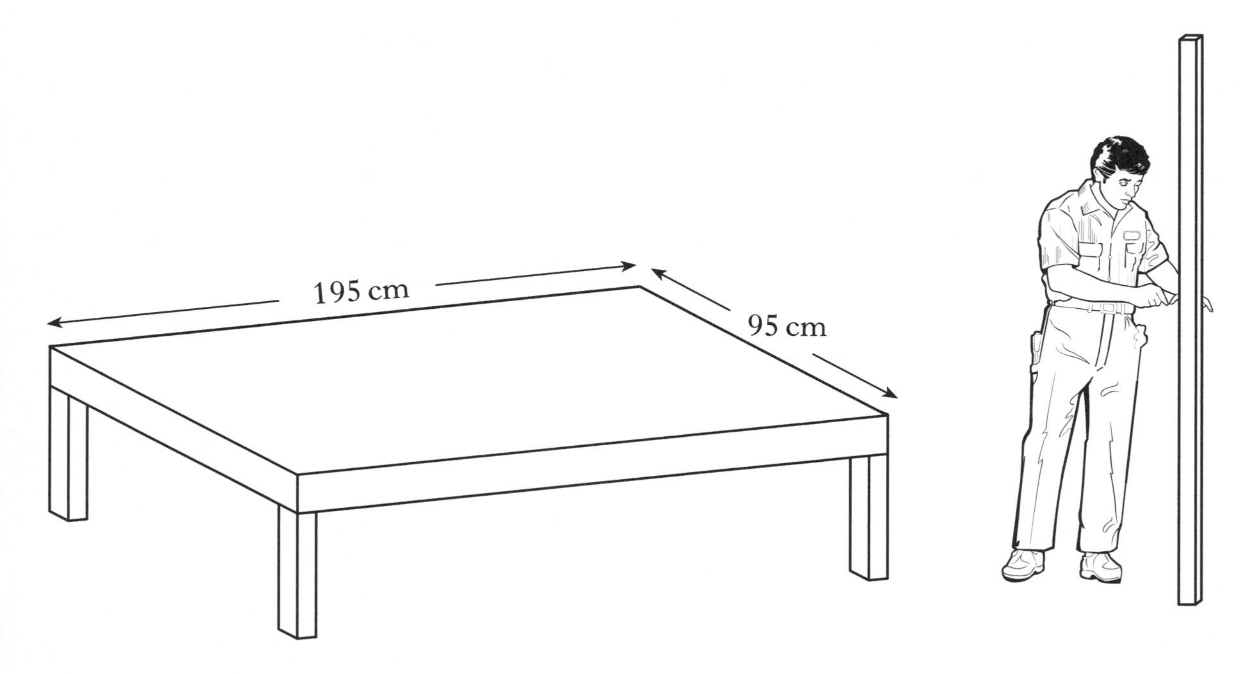

To make the frame rigid, Phil is going to add a piece of wood along one of its diagonals.

He has a piece of wood 2·2 metres long.

Is this piece of wood long enough to fit along the diagonal?

Give a reason for your answer.

Do not use a scale drawing.

4

[Turn over

DO NOT WRITE IN THIS MARGIN

Marks

10. Curtis flew from New York to London where he changed 1400 dollars into pounds.

He spent £650 in London and then changed the rest into euros before travelling to Paris.

How many euros did Curtis receive?

Exchange Rates

$	£1 = 1·75 dollars
€	£1 = 1·38 euros

3

DO NOT WRITE IN THIS MARGIN

Marks

11. Three roads form a right angled triangle as shown in the diagram.

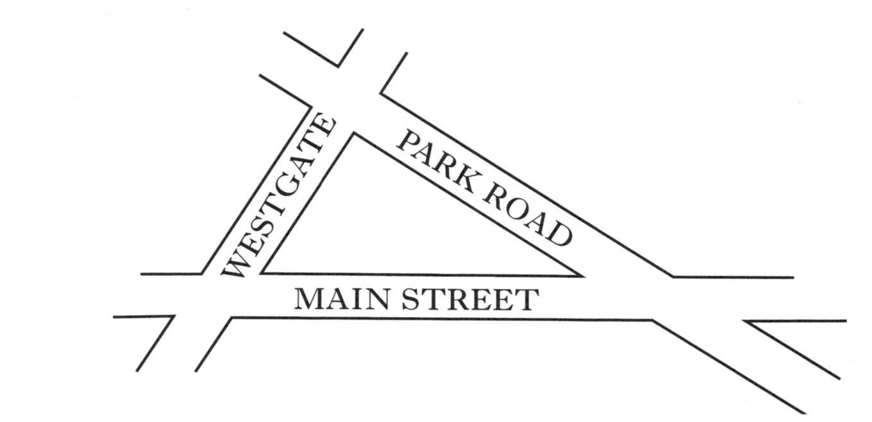

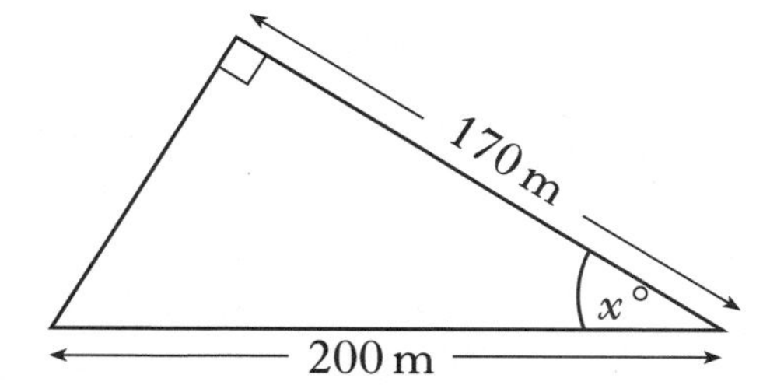

- Main Street is 200 metres long.
- Park Road is 170 metres long.
- The angle between Westgate and Park Road is 90 °.

The size of the angle between Main Street and Park Road is x °.

Calculate x.

Give your answer to **one decimal place**.

4

[Turn over

DO NOT WRITE IN THIS MARGIN

Marks

12. Pamela paid £40 for a concert ticket.

She was unable to go to the concert, so she sold her ticket on the Internet for £26.

Express her loss as a percentage of what she paid for the ticket.

4

DO NOT WRITE IN THIS MARGIN

Marks

13. The diagram below shows a birthday card.

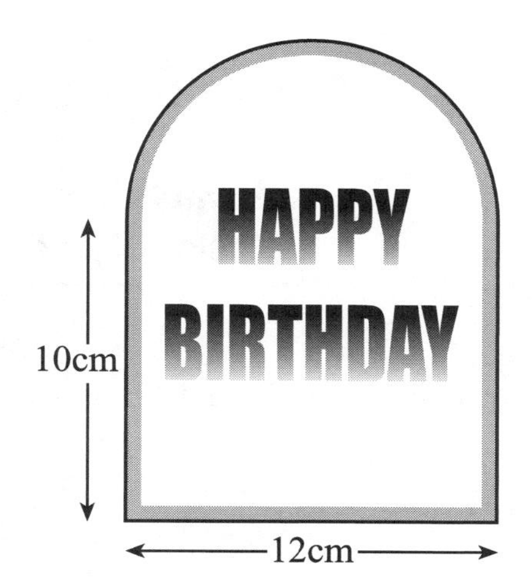

The card consists of a rectangle and a semi-circle.

There is gold ribbon all round the border of the card.

Calculate the total length of gold ribbon needed for this card.

Give your answer to the **nearest centimetre**.

5

[Turn over for Question 14 on *Page fourteen*

DO NOT WRITE IN THIS MARGIN

Marks

14. The tariffs shown below are available when buying a mobile phone.

Pay As You Go
Calls: 14p per minute

Monthly Contract
Rental: £18 per month
Calls: 6p per minute

(*a*) Find the cost of using 200 minutes of calls each month on the:

(i) Pay As You Go tariff;

(ii) Monthly Contract tariff. **2**

(*b*) Nick and Amy have mobile phones.

Nick is on Pay As You Go and Amy has a Monthly Contract.

In April:

- the cost to each was exactly the same
- Nick used the same number of minutes as Amy.

How many minutes was this? **3**

[*END OF QUESTION PAPER*]

DO NOT WRITE IN THIS MARGIN

ADDITIONAL SPACE FOR ANSWERS

DO NOT WRITE IN THIS MARGIN

ADDITIONAL SPACE FOR ANSWERS

[BLANK PAGE]

[BLANK PAGE]

[BLANK PAGE]

[BLANK PAGE]